Quick

———

and

———

Easy

———

Math

———

0

78

1

2

3 4

56

9

Quick and Easy Math

Isaac Asimov

Houghton Mifflin Company Boston

To copyreaders everywhere
who deserve so much credit
and get so little

FOURTH PRINTING   C

CONTENTS

Author's Note

THIS BOOK describes methods for solving arithmetical problems by "quick and easy" routes. These are not intended to replace the more systematic methods familiar to everyone but to supplement them.

It is customary in books such as this to include many exercises to develop the reader's confidence and skill in handling these easy but possibly new techniques. However, such exercises would clutter the book and reduce the room available for explaining the principles behind the methods; and it is crucial, in my opinion, to explain these principles thoroughly.

I think it is fair to assume that anyone interested enough in the subject to read this book will have the wit and energy to make exercises of his own. Better yet, I hope he will take the trouble to exercise the methods described in this book on all arithmetical problems that come his way in day-to-day life.

At first this may actually slow him. Through sheer lack of practice these short cuts may take more time than would the "tried-and-true" methods. Let him bear up, though. With a little patience, he will find himself racing through to correct results in practically no time and with practically no pain.

ISAAC ASIMOV

1

Why Shortcuts?

I SUPPOSE we have all heard of "mental marvels" who could add long columns of figures in a flash and do complicated calculations in their head. Perhaps we've even wished we could do so in order to astonish our friends, and have thought that if we only took a little time and effort, we could learn how. Actually, it doesn't take a genius or a good mathematician to do such calculations. To be sure, some great mathematicians and some extremely intelligent men have indeed been able to perform mental calculations in quick time, but others have not been able to do so. Albert Einstein always claimed he was poor at calculations and that he had trouble making out his income tax.

Then, too, there have been many cases of people without any education, and without much real intelligence, who were able to perform all sorts of mathematical tricks. Some were illiterate and could make nothing of themselves in their lives except for earning money by putting on exhibitions of calculation.

But if it doesn't take education or intelligence to be a lightning calculator, what does it take? Is it a matter of learning a few easy tricks with figures?

Apparently not. Lightning calculators seem to have unusually good memories for figures. If they multiply two large numbers, they seem to be able to "write down" the different steps in their minds as you would on paper. They seem to remember what they "write down" even, in some cases, if they have to stop the calculations for a considerable period of time. They can always go back to it afterward and continue, as you would if you wrote it on paper.

Yet memories can be trained. If you are not born with a miraculous one, you can still exercise what you do have and make it better. And then there are surely tricks and shortcuts in calculation. If you can learn those, too, would you not be set? Perhaps so, if you did two things. First, you must memorize all the short-cut rules for calculation. This is not hard if you're really serious about it and apply yourself, but in itself it is not enough.

A magician can show you how to manipulate cards so as to make whole decks seem to appear in your hand out of nowhere, but you will have to practise constantly; first to make your fingers nimble enough for the task and then to keep them so. You can learn how to read music in a day and discover just exactly which piano key to hit for every note shown; but to become a good pianist you must practise every day for years.

And that is the second step, then, after you have learned the rules: you must practise constantly. Even those few who are born "mental marvels" improve as they grow older and practise the art. Some of them keep at it, practising every day. If they were to stop, their ability would begin to fade off.

Yet, even though you may memorize the rules and practise daily, the chances are that you will not become a lightning calculator. After all, many people study piano and practise every day, but very few go on to become great concert pianists.

Well, then, if all that is so, why am I bothering to write a book on *Quick and Easy Math* — a book that is to be full of methods for making calculations simpler and more rapid? The answer is that we are faced every day with small calculations that often take up unnecessary time. You may have to be a mental marvel to look at a long chain of large numbers and add them in a flash, but you don't have to be one to look at $69 + 36$ and see in a flash that the answer is 105. Or you can be presented with the problem of multiplying 64 and 25 and say 1600 at once, without putting pencil to paper. Or you can find that 6% of $15 is 90¢ without pain or trouble.

It's the little things that count. You may not be able to put on exhibitions with the ability to multiply 64 and 25; you may not even be able to astonish your friends more than once or twice. However, you *can* make life easier for yourself and save yourself time and errors.

You may feel, though, that you *know* how to add $69 + 36$ and get 105 as an answer. You were taught how, long ago, in school. Was the "school method" wrong? If better and quicker methods exist, why weren't they taught in school?

School methods, of course, are *not* wrong; but usually they are longer than they have to be. For this there are two reasons. In the first place, school methods are intended mainly for written calculations, and the rules taught in school have you write down practically every step of the calculation. This is important for youngsters in the early grades who are just learning to handle numbers. Short-cut methods, on the other hand, depend often on the ability to manipulate numbers quickly in the head without writing them down. Most people can't do that easily until they have learned enough about number manipulation according to the long-drawn-out written methods.

By that time, the school methods have come to seem natural. In the early grades, children are drilled constantly in simple calculations by the school methods, over and over. Later on, when short-cut methods are introduced they may prefer the old, comfortable ways, even though the shortcut is really easier.

In the second place, if school methods are slow, they are also safe. They *always* work. If you follow the rules taught you in school for multiplication, you can multiply any two numbers that exist. It may take time, it may be very tedious, but you will get your answer. All you have to learn is the multiplication table and a certain set method of "carrying" and "indenting."

Short-cut methods, on the contrary, usually apply

only to certain types of calculation. One short-cut method can be applied to multiplications by 8 or 16, but not to multiplications by 7 or 15. There is a good method for dividing by 25 quickly, but not for dividing by 23 quickly. You therefore have to pick and choose shortcuts, and this places a great deal of responsibility on you. It takes more thought but you are repaid eventually by speed, if only you are patient at first.

I will suppose, then, that you are already familiar with the school methods of addition, subtraction, multiplication, and division and are willing to spend a little time trying to learn some special methods that will make calculation even easier.

For my part, I will try to make the book more than merely a list of rules. The rules exist, of course, but they are based on the manner in which numbers behave; that is, on the principles of arithmetic. It is more important to understand the principles than simply to memorize rules. Things that are memorized without real understanding are easily forgotten, and once forgotten can't be reconstructed. If, on the other hand, the rules you memorize arise out of the principles of arithmetic, then those rules seem natural and are easy to remember. Even if you forget them, you can reconstruct them from your knowledge of the principles.

You've got to remember the principles, but the principles make sense and are therefore easy to remember. Furthermore, the principles that have to be kept in mind are few in number, and out of them a large number of rules can be constructed.

Occasionally I will illustrate the principles by making use of algebraic symbols, simply because that is the shortest way of representing them. However, you may skip the algebra if you choose. It helps, but it is not essential.

Let us start, then, as one always does, with the simplest of the arithmetical operations — addition.

Addition

ADDITION is the first arithmetical operation learned in school, and the youngster begins by being drilled in the addition of digits until he has completely memorized the results of such addition. (A digit is a number made up of a single symbol. We use ten of them: 0, 1, 2, 3, 4, 5, 6, 7, 8, and 9.)

As a result we all know that $6 + 1 = 7$ and $8 + 4 = 12$. Indeed, we can tell at a glance the answers to all the hundred one-digit additions from $0 + 0$ to $9 + 9$. We have in effect memorized the "addition table." This is done so early in life that hardly any of us are even aware that there is such a thing as an addition table.

Once the addition table is memorized we are able to add any list of numbers, no matter how many there are and no matter how many digits each possesses. Suppose, for instance, we wanted to add

$$\begin{array}{r} 62 \\ +36 \\ \hline \end{array}$$

It is only necessary to add up the two vertical combinations, so that $2 + 6 = 8$ and $6 + 3 = 9$. The problem therefore works out as follows:

$$
\begin{array}{r}
62 \\
+36 \\
\hline
98
\end{array}
$$

In exactly the same way, we can work out the following:

$$
\begin{array}{r}
623,107 \\
+134,891 \\
\hline
757,998
\end{array}
$$

If we want to add three numbers, as in $12 + 32 + 54$, and make use only of the addition table, we can add them one addition at a time. Thus, $12 + 32 = 44$ and $44 + 54 = 98$.

This far, all seems so simple that there is no room for any method of making matters "quick and easy." Addition is quick and easy to begin with. However, we are about to come to a few difficulties, and before doing so, let's learn some names to use for the numbers and parts of numbers being added. The names are not commonly used in everyday life, but they are handy just the same. They give me a way of referring to a particular number or part of a number without having to say "the first number I mentioned" or "the column two from the right."

In the problem

$$\begin{array}{r} 62 \\ +36 \\ \hline 98 \end{array}$$

the number 62 is the "augend" (aw'jend) from a Latin word meaning "to increase." The augend, in other words, is the number to be increased through addition. The number 36 is the "addend"; that is, the number "to be added." (If more than two numbers are involved in addition, all but the first are called addends.) The solution to the addition, 98 in this case, is the "sum." This is from a Latin word meaning "highest" for, of course, the sum is the highest number involved in an ordinary addition.

In addition it doesn't matter how you arrange the numbers to be added. The sum remains the same. Thus, $62 + 36 = 98$, and $36 + 62 = 98$ also. (In algebraic symbols, we would say that $a + b = b + a$.) This means that the 62 can be either augend or addend, and the same is true for 36. For this reason, it often happens that all the numbers being summed are lumped together as addends. I, however, shall continue to call the first number the augend so that I can refer to it easily.

Not only do different numbers in an addition have their own particular names, but different parts of a number have their own names, too. Consider once again

$$
\begin{array}{r}
623,107 \\
+134,891 \\
\hline
757,998
\end{array}
$$

Suppose that you think of the three numbers making up this problem as consisting of vertical columns of digits. The column at the extreme right (7, 1, 8) is the "units column" and the one to its left (0, 9, 9) is the "tens column." Proceeding steadily leftward, we have the "hundreds column," the "thousands column," and the "ten thousands column." The one at the extreme left in this case is the "hundred thousands column." If we had even larger numbers to deal with, we would have a "millions column," a "ten millions column," and so on.

Now we are ready to consider the point at which certain difficulties arise in addition.

CARRYING

Suppose that instead of adding 62 and 36, we wished to add 68 and 76. If we do exactly as we did before, we find that $8 + 6 = 14$ and $6 + 7 = 13$. The sum in each case is a two-digit number. We place the right-hand digit under the digits being added and allow the left-hand digit to push over into the column to the left.

$$
\begin{array}{r}
68 \\
+ \ 76 \\
\hline
14 \\
13 \\
\hline
144
\end{array}
$$

The 14 and the 13 are the "partial sums" and, when properly arranged, can be added to give the final sum of 144.

This may puzzle you, because you may think that this is not the way you have been taught to add 68 and 76. However, it is! You are taught early in grade school not to write out the 14. You are told to "put down 4 and carry 1." Then you add 6 and 7 *and* the 1 you have carried, so that $6 + 7 + 1 = 14$:

$$
\begin{array}{r}
68 \\
+\ 76 \\
\scriptstyle 1 \\
\hline
144
\end{array}
$$

This is exactly what I've done before, except that the 1 of the 14 is placed (as a small number) in the tens column instead of among the partial sums. A more complicated example of an addition, first with all the partial sums written out and then with the use of carrying is this:

$$
\begin{array}{r}
5,672 \\
+\ 4,981 \\
+\ 2,169 \\
\hline
12 \\
21 \\
1\ 6 \\
11 \\
\hline
12,822
\end{array}
\qquad
\begin{array}{r}
5,672 \\
+\ 4,981 \\
+\ 2,169 \\
\scriptstyle 1\ 21 \\
\hline
12,822
\end{array}
$$

It is the carrying of numbers that confuses people. They try to keep it in their head and at the crucial moment forget; or else remember that something must be carried but forget whether it is 1 or 2; or else they write down little numbers (as I have done above) which are sometimes hard to read and one number is confused with another. Naturally, the more complicated the addition the more likely it is that such difficulties may arise.

Is there any way, then, in which we can eliminate carrying? Even if we could eliminate it only some of the time, we would end with a great saving in time and tension.

Well, let's think about carrying in general. The larger a digit, the more likely it is to involve carrying. The digit 9, when added to any digit but 0, will make carrying necessary. On the other hand, a small digit is easy to handle and 0 is the easiest of all. No matter what digit you add to a 0, even a 9, no carrying is involved.

The first rule in making math quick and easy is to change something difficult into something easy, whenever that is possible. Therefore, is there any way of changing a large digit into a small one? In particular, in adding 68 and 76, it is the 8 which gives the trouble. Is there any way of changing it to a small digit; best of all, to a 0?

The easiest way to do that is to add 2 to 68, and make it 70. But if you change 68 to 70, aren't you altering the problem? You want to add 68 and 76, not 70 and 76. Perfectly correct, but perhaps you can do something to the 76 to balance what you have done to the 68. You have added 2 to 68, therefore subtract 2 from 76. Having done these things, you will not have altered the sum.

You can see this if you make use of some very simple algebra. The sum of a and b is $a + b$. Suppose you add any number (n) to a and subtract that same number from b. The number a becomes $a + n$ while b becomes $b - n$. Add the two numbers together thus: $a + n + b - n$ and the answer is still $a + b$ as before. If you subtract n from a and add it to b, the sum is $a - n + b + n$, and that too works out to $a + b$.

In short, you can add a particular number to the augend and subtract it from the addend without altering the sum; or you can subtract a particular number from the augend and add it to the addend without altering the sum.

In any addition, what we are really interested in is the sum, and provided that sum is unchanged we can do anything we want to the augend and addend. Why not, then, pick out something to do to them which will eliminate carrying and will simplify the addition?

Instead of adding 68 and 76, we can add 70 and 74 (adding 2 to the augend and subtracting 2 from the addend) so that the answer, 144, is clear in a flash, without carrying. We might also have subtracted 4 from the augend and added 4 to the addend, so as to change 6 to a 0. Instead of adding 68 and 76, we would be adding 64 and 80, and the answer, 144, would still be clear in a flash.

In this first example of quick and easy math, let me make two points. First, you may wonder which change you *ought* to make. Ought you to change 68 + 76 to 70 + 74 or to 64 + 80? The proper answer is that there is no "ought" about it. Do as you please. Both changes are based on the same arithmetical principle and both give you the same correct answer. You need only choose the change you prefer. I myself would change 68 + 76 to 70 + 74 because to add and subtract 2 seems easier to me than to add and subtract 4. However, your mind need not necessarily work the way mine does, and you may like to add and subtract 4. In which case, go ahead.

Second, it takes me a long time to explain a rule for making an operation quick and easy. This does *not* mean that the rule is long and complicated. It just means that I am concerned with making the rule as clear as possible and making sure you see the arithmetical principles on which it is based. Once the rule is clear, you will find it easy to apply — and much, much quicker to use than to explain.

ADDING LEFT TO RIGHT

You may think, Yes, but these are very small additions. What if I have a string of numbers to add?

In the first place, remember that most of the time you will be faced with the addition of two numbers. If you learn to avoid carrying in such simple cases, you will avoid perhaps nine tenths of all the errors made in addition.

Next, even when you add more than two numbers, you may well be adding them two at a time. Suppose you are asked to add 55, 76, and 39, for instance. You can do it the long way and say, "First, 5 and 6 is 11 and 9 is 20. Put down 0 and carry 2. Then, 5 and 7 is 12 and 3 is 15 and how much did I carry? Oh, yes, 2. That means 15 and 2 is 17 and the answer is 170."

Instead, you might also do it this way: $55 + 76 + 39$, begins with $55 + 76$, which is the same as $60 + 71 = 131$. Then, $131 + 39$ is the same as $130 + 40 = 170$.

Here is something else. If you should happen to be faced with a long string of figures, are you sure you need the exact answer? We sometimes imagine we must solve all problems exactly, to the last tiny figure. In everyday life, however, we sometimes don't have to be exact. Suppose the following string of numbers represents the prices (in dollars) of various articles that must be bought:

$$
\begin{array}{r}
13,667 \\
5,687 \\
21,112 \\
10,377 \\
9,898 \\
5,100 \\
11,132 \\
\hline
33 \\
34 \\
2\,6 \\
24 \\
5 \\
\hline
76,973
\end{array}
$$

Notice that I have written down all the partial sums. If we did it by the usual method of carrying, we would start with the units column at the extreme right. That would add up to 33, so we would "put down 3 and carry 3"; the 3 being carried to the tens column. The tens column would add up to 37 (counting the 3 we had carried), so we would put down 7 and carry 3 into the hundreds column, and so on.

When we add a string of numbers, with carrying, we come to think that there is some sort of rigid law making it absolutely necessary for us to start with the units column and work toward the left, column by column. If, however, we don't carry, but write out all the partial sums, we find that it doesn't matter which column we add first. The string of numbers I gave you could be added in either of the following ways or any of a hundred seventeen others:

13,667	13,667
5,687	5,687
21,112	21,112
10,377	10,377
9,898	9,898
5,100	5,100
11,132	11,132
2 6	34
33	2 6
24	5
5	33
34	24
76,973	76,973

In the example on the left, I added up the hundreds column first, then the units, and so on. In the example on the right, I added up the tens column first, then the hundreds, and so forth. It doesn't matter in what order we add the columns; the answer comes out the same.

Why, then, are we taught to start from the units column and work to the left? That is because we are also taught to carry, and because if we carry we can only be sure of the numbers we actually write down (if we remember to start at the right and work left).

You see, numbers that are carried are taken from a particular column into the column on its left. This means that the sum of a given column can be altered by what happens in the column to its right, but cannot be altered by what happens in the column to its left.

Suppose, in the example we have been considering, we added up the ten thousands column (the one at the extreme left) first. We would say $1 + 2 + 1 + 1 = 5$, and write down 5. If we then proceeded to the thousands column, which is the next one to the right, we would say that $3 + 5 + 1 + 0 + 9 + 5 + 1 = 24$. Now we would put down 4 and carry 2. This means that the 5 we had already written down would have to be changed to a 7. If we then went one column farther to the right, we would find that the 4 we had written down under the thousands column would have to be changed to a 6.

Watch, though, what happens if we add up the units column first, the one at the extreme right. Now we say that $7 + 7 + 2 + 7 + 8 + 0 + 2 = 33$, which means we put down 3 and carry 3. The 3 which we have put down is going to stay no matter what else happens in the addition, because there is no column to the right of the units column to supply a number to carry. Furthermore, the 3 we have carried into the tens column is the *only* number that will be carried there.

We add up the tens column: $6 + 8 + 1 + 7 + 9 + 0 + 3$ and add the carried 3 to that, so that the sum is 37. We put down 7 and carry 3. The 7 we have put down is permanent because the only thing that can change it is a number carried over from the units column, and that has already been carried over. As for the 3 which has now been carried over into the hundreds column, that is all we will have to be concerned with there, and so on.

By starting at the right and working to the left, then, you can proceed without making any changes in the numbers you actually write down. You needn't erase or cross out (provided you make no errors.)

But this also means that you must deal with the units before you deal with the tens, and with the tens before you deal with the hundreds, and so on. But the tens column is more important than the units column, and the hundreds column is still more important (a mistake in the hundreds column might give you an answer that was off by 300, whereas the same mistake in the units column would give an answer that was only off by 3).

For the sake of the increased importance at the left

end of the figures, it is sometimes better to start there, even if it does mean you will have to change the numbers you write down.

Suppose, for instance, you happen to have $40,000 available for purchases and you want to know if you can buy everything on the list. You don't care what the exact total is. You only want to know if it comes to more than $40,000 or not. In that case, what's the use of carefully adding up the units column?

Instead, you start with the ten thousands column at the extreme left. Adding that, you find that $1 + 2 + 1 + 1 = 5$. Changes may be made in that 5 as a result of carrying numbers, if you proceed in the addition, but those changes can only serve to increase the 5, never to decrease it. By adding the first column, we know immediately that the sum is at least $50,000. That means it is more than $40,000 and we need proceed no further with the addition.

Or suppose you have $72,000 and want to know if that's enough. Starting at the ten thousands column as before and finding a total of 5, we proceed to the thousands column immediately to its right. This gives a total of 24. We can write down the 4 and carry the 2, and that carried 2 must change the 5 in the ten thousands column to a 7. Now we know that the sum is at least $74,000 and again we can stop.

If you start at the left and proceed to the right, adding the partial sums as you go, the result would be as follows:

$$
\begin{array}{r}
13{,}667 \\
5{,}687 \\
21{,}112 \\
10{,}377 \\
9{,}898 \\
5{,}100 \\
11{,}132 \\
\hline
5 \\
24 \\
\hline
74 \\
2\,6 \\
\hline
76\,6 \\
34 \\
\hline
76\,94 \\
33 \\
\hline
76{,}973
\end{array}
$$

Each column you add gets you closer to the answer, calculating from the important end: $50,000, $74,000, $76,000, $76,940, and, finally, $76,973.

Let's compare the two directions of addition. If you start at the right, you must go all the way to the left, because the columns grow more important the farther leftward you go. However, you end with an exact answer. If you start at the left, you can quit at any time, as soon as you have the information you need. However, if you quit before adding all the columns, you will not have the exact answer.

Notice, by the way, that in adding from the left to the right, you will have to be changing the values of your sum constantly. It may strike you that it is too much to expect a person to carry all these changing figures in his head.

Quite so, at least at first. With practice you'll be able to, but to begin with you will certainly have to write down numbers. Otherwise, you'll be sure to make mistakes. But what of that? There is no particular rule that says that quick and easy math *must* be done in the head. Many operations can be, but not necessarily all. If you find you must write down numbers, but that the process takes less time than the long-way-round school method, you are still the gainer.

For example if you want to add $34 + 86 + 154 + 72 + 69$, it is not really difficult, with practice, to look at the list and come to the answer 415. However, you may prefer to add the numbers two at a time, writing down the partial sums as you go. Since $34 + 86 = 120 + 154 = 274 + 72 = 346 + 69 = 415$, you write down 120, 274, 346, 415, just to keep things straight. You are not cheating; you are just being cautious. Eventually, you may not need to do this.

And of course you make use of simplifications as you go. You change $34 + 86$ to $30 + 90$; $346 + 69$ to $345 + 70$, and so on.

ROUND NUMBERS

Suppose you are only interested in an approximate answer and don't want to trouble yourself by adding from left to right. It may be that you are so used to adding from right to left you don't want to fight the habit. Is there another way out of having to add up columns you don't need? Yes, there is; another and, in some ways, an even better way.

The one time we don't need to worry about adding up a column of digits is when all those digits are zeros. The sum of any number of zeros is still zero, and such a sum can be written down without labor or thought.

What we want to do, then, is to change the digits in the unwanted columns to zeros and to do so while changing the value of the original number as little as possible. Suppose we go back to the long addition we dealt with in the previous section and assume we are only interested in the answer to the nearest thousand. In that case why bother with the hundreds column, the tens column, or the units column? Change the digits in those columns to zeros.

If we take the first number 13,667, we can change that to 13,000. In doing so we have decreased the number by 667. Suppose, however, that we change 13,667 to 14,000. Now we have increased the value of the number, but only by 333. The latter change is the better one. In the same way we can change 5687 to 6000, 21,112 to 21,000, 10,377 to 10,000, 9898 to 10,000, 5100 to 5000, and 11,132 to 11,000.

If we compare a number like 6000 with a number like 5687, we say that the former is a "round number." This goes back to the ancient feeling that a circle is the perfect figure and that roundness therefore signifies perfection. The number 6000 represents an exact number of thousands and 5687 does not. The former is therefore "round." Of course, round numbers usually end with one or more zeros and the symbol for zero is a circle or an oval, so "round number" has a new kind of meaning in that light.

When 5687 is changed to 6000 it is being "rounded off to the nearest thousand." It might also be rounded off to the nearest ten and be written as 5690, or to the nearest hundred and written as 5700.

Adding up the figures, we have, after rounding them off to the nearest thousand:

$$
\begin{array}{r}
14,000 \\
6,000 \\
21,000 \\
10,000 \\
10,000 \\
5,000 \\
11,000 \\
\hline
77,000
\end{array}
$$

The three columns on the right are all zeros and add up to zeros. We are left with the first two columns containing digits other than zero, and these can be added up quickly (even mentally). Moreover, the final, rounded answer is 77,000 as compared with the actual sum of 76,973. The difference is only 27.

In general, adding round numbers gives a more accurate answer than adding left-to-right, if the same number of columns is added in each case. The reason for this is not hard to see.

In left-to-right addition of exact numbers, we add each column without worrying about any changes that would be produced by carrying. The figure that is eventually carried, however, always increases the sum. For this reason, the sum we get by adding left-to-right is always *less* than the real sum. If only one or two columns are added, the sum obtained may be considerably less than the actual sum.

In the example given in the previous section, the actual answer is 76,973, but if we add up only the first column on the left the answer we get is 50,000. If we add up the first two columns, the answer is 74,000; if we add up the first three, it is 76,000; and if we add up the first four, it is 76,940. Even after adding up four columns left-to-right, we have not come as close to the actual answer as we did in adding two columns of digits by the round-number method.

In rounding off a number, you see, you sometimes increase it and sometimes decrease it. Thus, 13,667 is changed to 14,000, an increase of 333, while 21,112 was changed to 21,000, a decrease of 112. In any long series of numbers, it is quite likely that the increases and decreases involved in rounding off will very nearly balance each other. This will leave the sum not very different from what it would have been in the first place.

(Of course, we never gain in one place without losing in another. The round-number method may be more accurate than the left-to-right method, but in the former you have to take time to change each number into the nearest round number, whereas in the latter you work with the numbers as they are.)

It is important to remember that the increases and decreases in rounding off are very likely to just about balance — but not certain to do so. It might just happen, for instance, that the following numbers are to be added: 13,575, 4065, 5551, and 7001. If you are interested in the answer to the nearest thousand, you can round off each number accordingly, and work out the sum of 14,000, 4000, 6000, and 7000. The rounded sum is 31,000 as compared with an actual sum of 30,192. The rounded sum is too large by 808, and that may be rather too far off for your liking.

The reason for such a large difference is that two of the numbers, when rounded, are decreased by very small amounts, while the other two are increased by quite large amounts. The increases, in this case, considerably overbalance the decreases.

If, then, you are rounding off a number to the nearest thousand and notice that you are going to make a rather large change, you might round it off to the nearest hundred instead. Instead of rounding 13,575 and 5551 to 14,000 and 6000 respectively, round them to 13,600 and 5600.

Now, if you add

$$
\begin{array}{r}
13,600 \\
4,000 \\
5,600 \\
7,000 \\
\hline
30,200
\end{array}
$$

the answer 30,200 is only 8 removed from 30,192. There is a considerable gain in accuracy for only very little extra in the way of work.

CHECKING ADDITION

After you have worked out the answer to an arithmetical calculation, particularly if it is a complicated one, the question arises: Is my answer correct?

It may be that you have worked out the answer exactly to the last place, but you just want to make sure there is no really big error — a small error won't be fatal. In that case you can repeat your addition by the round-number method in order to see if you get about the answer you had before. If you do, there are no big mistakes anyway. More likely, though, you are interested in the exact answer and don't want to make any mistake, large or small. What then?

What most people do then is to "go over it." They repeat the calculation a second time and even a third time, going through all the steps and making sure they have made no mistake. Unfortunately, repeating a calculation exactly as before is not the best way to catch a mistake.

Suppose that you have the following addition:

$$3,145$$
$$272$$
$$18,146$$
$$1,987$$
$$322$$

You decide to add these numbers right-to-left. You start with the units column, adding downward, and keeping the partial sums in your head as everyone does. You say, therefore, 5, 7, 14, 21, 23, put down 3 and carry 2. In doing this you have already made a mistake: $5 + 2 = 7$, but $7 + 6 = 13$, not 14.

You know very well that $7 + 6 = 13$ and you may feel certain you would never say $7 + 6 = 14$. Yet, you might. Notice that when you are adding 7 and 6 the next number you are going to add will be a 7. Your eye may see that 7 and automatically your mind might add it rather than the 6 and, of course, $7 + 7 = 14$. The result is that you arrive at an answer of 23,873 instead of 23,872.

If you decided to check your answer and begin the calculation in precisely the same way as before, there is a good chance that you might again say 5, 7, 14, 21, 23. It may be that the mind remembers the sequence of numbers as worked out originally (even though you may not realize you remember it) and takes the easy way out of repeating it without actually doing the calculation again.

In any case, it is not at all unusual to have a person make the same quite silly mistake over and over again as he repeats a calculation. Anyone can do that — make a simple error first, then repeat it when checking. A professor of mathematics can do it as well as a beginner. It is better, then, in repeating an addition, to reach the sum by a different route. In that way, the number combinations would be different and there would be no reason to make the same error you made before.

Since it doesn't matter in what order you add a series of digits, why do it from the top down? In checking, why not do it from the bottom up? If you add upward, beginning with the units column, you say, 2, 9, 15, 17, 22, put down 2 and carry 2. At once you see a discrepancy; you had put down a 3 the first time.

That won't tell you, of course, whether your first answer was wrong. The first answer may have been perfectly correct, and you may have made an error in checking. But the fact that you arrived at two different answers means there is something wrong and you must inspect your addition carefully.

Naturally, it is to be hoped (and, I think, expected) that you will not make any mistakes. In that case, the sum of the numbers added from the bottom up should be the same as that obtained when the numbers are added from the top down. It is perfectly natural to assume then that your answer is correct, and you need investigate it no further.

It may happen, though, that you may make one mistake while adding from the top down and another mistake while adding from the bottom up and that these two different mistakes will give you the same wrong answer. This is possible, but very unlikely, and few people worry about such a chance at all.

Checking a calculation by repeating it, whether by the same route or by a different route, doubles the amount of time spent on the calculation. For this reason most people don't bother checking the addition of long columns of figures; they seem to prefer to take their chances on errors.

Perhaps if there were a short-cut way to see if a long complicated addition needs checking —

Well, there is.

Consider the following,

$$
\begin{array}{r}
8{,}921 \\
+\ 4{,}135 \\
\hline
13{,}056
\end{array}
$$

and suppose you add up the digits of the augend, 8921. You have $8 + 9 + 2 + 1 = 20$. Add up the digits of this sum: $2 + 0 = 2$. Do the same for the other numbers involved in the addition, always continuing to add until you have but a single digit left, and let's call the digit we finally reach in this manner the "digit sum."

Thus, the digit sum of the addend (4135) is $4 + 1 + 3 + 5 = 13$; $1 + 3 = 4$. That of the sum (13,056) is $1 + 3 + 0 + 5 + 6 = 15$; $1 + 5 = 6$.

Let's repeat the addition now, placing the digit sum to the right of each number:

$$\begin{array}{r} 8{,}921 \\ +\ 4{,}135 \\ \hline 13{,}056 \end{array} \qquad \begin{array}{c} 2 \\ 4 \\ \hline 6 \end{array}$$

You can't help noticing that the digit sums add up correctly. This is no coincidence; it always happens.

Try another one:

$$\begin{array}{r} 5{,}633 \\ +\ 4{,}903 \\ \hline 10{,}536 \end{array} \qquad \begin{array}{c} 8 \\ 7 \\ \hline 6 \end{array}$$

The digit sum of the augend is $5 + 6 + 3 + 3 = 17$; $1 + 7 = 8$. The digit sum of the addend is $4 + 9 + 0 + 3 = 16$; $1 + 6 = 7$. The digit sum of the sum is $1 + 0 + 5 + 3 + 6 = 15$; $1 + 5 = 6$. However, $8 + 7$ does not equal 6. Perhaps not, if we are dealing with actual numbers, but we are dealing with digit sums. Thus, $8 + 7 = 15$ and $1 + 5 = 6$. In digit-sum calculations, then, we can say that $8 + 7 = 6$.

Whenever you add up a column of figures to get a correct sum, you will find that the digit sums will form a correct addition, too. If, therefore, you have completed an addition, it is not necessary to check by repeating the calculation. You can work out the digit sums and see if they form a correct addition. If so, you can be almost sure the answer is correct.

Unfortunately, you cannot be positively sure. Suppose the correct answer is 10,536 and its digit sum is 6, as in the last example given. But there are many other numbers with a digit sum of 6. These include 10,563, 15,036, 65,310, 11,112, 60,000, 24, and so on.

It is quite unlikely, however, that mistakes made in addition will produce a wrong answer with the same digit sum as the right answer. It is much more likely that the digit sum will be altered. You will then find yourself faced with a digit-sum addition such as $2 + 3 = 7$ or $4 + 8 = 2$, which are wrong. After all, $2 + 3 = 5$ and $4 + 8 = 12$ and $1 + 2 = 3$; so that $4 + 8 = 3$.

You can then be quite certain that somewhere in your addition there is a mistake.

To be sure, adding up the digits of each number takes time. Fortunately, working out the digit sum can be simplified one step further. This simplification depends on the fact that adding 9 never alters the digit sum. Thus, $13 + 9 = 22$ and the digit sum of both 13 and 22 is 4; $175 + 9 = 184$ and the digit sum of both 175 and 184 is 4; $4658 + 9 = 4667$ and the digit sum of both 4658 and 4667 is 5. In fact, no matter how many times we add 9 to a number we don't change the digit sum. Consider that $72 + 9 + 9 + 9 + 9 = 108$ and the digit sum of both 72 and 108 is 9.

Therefore, in adding up the digits in any number, why bother to include any 9, since adding it won't change the digit sum? For that matter, why bother to include a set of smaller numbers which add up to 9? If we add the digits of 8921 we get 20 and $2 + 0 = 2$. However, if we eliminate the 9 to begin with and then the $8 + 1$ because that adds up to 9, we are left only with the 2. We arrive at the same digit sum with much less time and effort.

Consider the following sum:

42,572	2
17,999	8
11,240	8
54,603	0
126,414	0

In the first number, you eliminate $5 + 4$, and $7 + 2$ and that leaves only the digit 2, which is the digit sum. In the second number you eliminate the three 9's and end with $1 + 7 = 8$. In the third number there is no elimination possible but $1 + 1 + 2 + 4$ is easy enough to add up to 8. In the fourth number you eliminate $5 + 4$ and $6 + 3$ and are left with 0. Finally, in the sum you can eliminate the $1 + 2 + 6$ and the $4 + 1 + 4$, since both sums add up to 9, and are again left with zero.

Now you must see if the digit-sum addition is correct. Is $2 + 8 + 8 + 0 = 0$? Well, the sum is 18 according to the ordinary system of arithmetic, but from that sum of 18, we can eliminate $1 + 8$ and are left with 0. The digit-sum addition is correct, and in all likelihood so is the actual addition.

Because 9's and digits adding up to 9 are eliminated from consideration, this method of checking addition is called "casting out nines."

The method of casting out nines is a quicker way of checking addition than by actually repeating the calculation. The longer and more complicated the addition, the more time is saved. Furthermore, many people find it entertaining to hunt down the 9's and watch the digit sums add up correctly and, after learning the method, check their additions for the fun of it.

Of course, there is no magic in casting out nines (although it may seem magical just at first). Let's see why it works. If we start with the single-digit numbers (0, 1, 2, 3, 4, 5, 6, 7, 8, 9) they all are their own digit sums except 9, which we cast out and for which we assign 0 as its digit sum. The digit sums, then, are 0, 1, 2, 3, 4, 5, 6, 7, 8, 0.

Now let's try the two-digit numbers (10, 11, 12, 13, 14, 15, 16, 17, 18, 19, 20, 21, and so on). If we write their digit sums in order (continuing to set 9's equal to 0), we find these to be 1, 2, 3, 4, 5, 6, 7, 8, 0, 1, 2. In fact, you can continue as long as you like (into the millions and billions, if you have the patience and time), and you will find that the digit sums go on forever like that — 0, 1, 2, 3, 4, 5, 6, 7, 8, 0, 1, 2, 3, 4, 5, 6, 7, 8, 0, 1, 2, 3, 4, 5, 6, 7, 8, 0, 1, on and on and on.

Furthermore, if you check the series you will find that every number that has the digit sum 0 is divisible by 9 without a remainder. (We shall take up division later in the book; I am sure you know enough about division to see that 9, 18, 27, 36, 54, and so on — all of which have digit sums of 0 — are also divisible by 9 without remainder.)

Since the digit sums increase in order by adding 1

each time (1, 2, 3, etc.), we can see that any number
which, when divided by 9 leaves a remainder of 1, has
a digit sum of 1. If it leaves a remainder of 2, it has a
digit sum of 2, and so on. The digit sums are just the
remainders left when a number is divided by 9.

In algebra, then, we can say that any number can be
written in the form, $9a + b$, where a is any number and
b is the digit sum of the entire number, $9a + b$. For
instance, take the number 214. If we divide it by 9,
the answer is 23 plus a remainder of 7. Therefore, 214
can be written $9(23) + 7$. The digit sum of the original
number is indeed 7.

Suppose we write two numbers, one as $9a + b$ and
the other as $9c + d$. If we add these, the total is
$9(a + c) + b + d$. The digit sum of the sum is therefore $b + d$ (which may be simplified further, of course).

In other words, in any addition which is correct $9a +
b + 9c + d = 9(a + c) + b + d$, the digit sums must
add up correctly too $(b + d = b + d)$.

As we shall see later, the other operations — subtraction, multiplication, and division — are all related to
addition. Subtraction is the reverse of addition; multiplication is a series of additions; and division is the reverse of multiplication. Therefore, if casting out nines
works for addition, it will also work for the other operations. In the proper places, I will demonstrate this.

3

Subtraction

WE can look upon subtraction as the reverse of addition. Suppose we know that $6 + 1 = 7$. Let us take that in reverse and look at the numbers from right to left. If we then change the plus sign $(+)$ to a minus sign $(-)$, we have $7 - 1 = 6$.

This is true in any number of cases. If $7 + 5 = 12$, then $12 - 5 = 7$; if $18 + 3 = 21$, then $21 - 3 = 18$. (In algebraic notation, we say that if $a + b = c$, then $c - b = a$.) This means that if we know the addition table from $0 + 0 = 0$ to $9 + 9 = 18$, we automatically know the "subtraction table" from $18 - 9 = 9$ to $0 - 0 = 0$.

(The word "plus," by the way, comes from a Latin word meaning "more," and "minus" comes from a Latin word meaning "less." Thus, if we say "seven plus some number" we will have an answer that is more than seven; while if we say "seven minus some number" we will have an answer that is less than seven.)

In a subtraction such as $12 - 5 = 7$, the first number, 12, is called the "minuend," from a Latin word meaning "to be made less." The minuend, you see, is to be made less as a result of the subtraction. The number 5 is the "subtrahend" from a Latin word meaning "that which is to be subtracted." The number 7 is the "difference." We can put it this way: the minuend minus the subtrahend equals the difference.

In the addition $a + b = c$, a and b can be any numbers at all, and c must then be larger than either a or b (unless either a or b is 0). The sum is the largest number in any addition. If the addition is reversed and converted into a subtraction, $c - b = a$, the sum becomes the minuend. Since the sum is the highest number in an addition, the minuend must be the highest number in a subtraction. In particular, it must be higher than the subtrahend, if the difference is to be greater than zero. (If the minuend is equal to the subtrahend, the difference is zero: $a - a = 0$.)

This means that you can't subtract any number from any number, at least not by the methods of grade school arithmetic. You can get an answer to $7 - 5$, or even to $7 - 7$, but not to $7 - 9$, for in the last case the minuend is smaller than the subtrahend. Once you study algebra, subtractions like $7 - 9$ are solved by introducing the notion of "negative numbers" — but we won't bother with that in this book.

However, even though the minuend may be larger than the subtrahend, there may be certain digits in the minuend that are smaller than certain digits in the subtrahend. This may or may not cause trouble.

If we line up a minuend and a subtrahend, units

column under units column, tens column under tens column, and so on, we would have no trouble if each digit in the minuend is larger than the digit immediately underneath in the subtrahend. The following shows what I mean:

$$\begin{array}{r} 72,998,476 \\ -61,818,034 \\ \hline 11,180,442 \end{array}$$

In such a subtraction, you can write down the difference as rapidly as you can move a pencil. What's more, it doesn't matter whether you go from right to left or from left to right.

It is when you get a subtraction like this

$$\begin{array}{r} 61 \\ -48 \\ \hline \end{array}$$

that you are likely to hesitate a bit, even though it involves far fewer digits than the first subtraction. The subtrahend, 48, is smaller than the minuend, 61, so the subtraction is quite legitimate. However, if we start with the units column, as we are taught to do in school, we face a problem at once, for 8 is larger than 1. The subtraction $1 - 8$ is not in our subtraction table.

To handle such a situation, we are therefore taught a system of "borrowing." Instead of subtracting 8 from 1, we borrow a 10 and add it to the 1 to make 11. Now we are subtracting 8 from 11 and get the answer 3, which we write down.

But where did the borrowed 10 come from? Naturally, it came from the tens column. To make up for that we must subtract 1 from the 6 in that tens column, making it 5. Now we subtract 4 from 5 (instead of 4 from the original 6). In subtracting 4 from 5, we get the difference 1, and write that down. In other words, $61 - 48 = 13$.

Here is another way of looking at it. The number 61 is actually $60 + 1$. It can also be considered $50 + 11$, so that we can actually consider "sixty-one" to be "fifty-eleven." Instead of writing $61 - 48$, we can write

$$
\begin{array}{r}
5(11) \\
-48 \\
\hline
13
\end{array}
$$

and, as you see, get 13 as the difference.

Instead of subtracting 1 from the 6 in the tens column of the minuend, we can add 1 to the 4 in the tens column of the subtrahend and make it

$$
\begin{array}{r}
6(11) \\
-58 \\
\hline
13
\end{array}
$$

and still get 13 as the difference.

Some grade schools teach the latter method, because that involves "carrying," which we have usually already learned and grown accustomed to in addition. If we are asked to solve $61 - 48$, we say something like this to ourselves: "Let's see now, 8 from 1 is impossible, so that makes it 8 from 11, leaving 3. Write down 3 and carry 1 and that makes the 4 into a 5. Take 5 from 6 and get 1, so the answer is 13."

Although this system is rather complicated at first, it becomes such second nature to most of us that we come to do it without ever trying to figure out why we do it. But because most people subtract without understanding the mechanics, they are likely to hesitate whenever it comes time to borrow and carry.

They may make mistakes, too. If a person isn't careful, the 6 − 4 in the tens column is going to strike him as coming to 2 so strongly that he may easily write 23 as the answer. Either he will forget to carry the 1 or, if he does carry it, he will forget to do anything with it. Almost all errors in subtraction involve the step in which we borrow and carry. Consequently, we should follow our first general rule of changing something difficult into something easy. If we don't want to make mistakes, let's try to avoid borrowing and carrying in subtraction if that is at all possible.

The one digit we can always subtract from any other digit without borrowing is 0. Therefore, let's try to place a 0 in the subtrahend of the subtraction problem we are discussing in place of the troublesome 8. If, in 61 − 48, we add 2 to the subtrahend and make it 50, we have our zero. But now we'll have to do something to the minuend to keep the difference from being changed.

In *adding* two numbers, you may remember, we were

able to keep the sum unchanged if we added a particular number to the augend and subtracted that same number from the addend. This won't work in subtraction. Thus $7 - 4 = 3$, but if you add 2 to the minuend and subtract 2 from the subtrahend, you have $9 - 2 = 7$. The difference has been changed.

Consider this, though. Not only is $7 - 4 = 3$, but $8 - 5 = 3$, and $9 - 6 = 3$ and $10 - 7 = 3$. If we add the same number to *both* minuend and subtrahend the difference remains unchanged. If we subtract the same number from both, the difference also remains unchanged.

We can express this algebraically. In the subtraction, $a - b$, suppose we add n to both numbers. The subtraction becomes $(a + n) - (b + n)$. Clearing parentheses, we have $a + n - b - n$; the n's cancel and the answer is still $a - b$. If we had subtracted n from both numbers, we would have $(a - n) - (b - n)$. This would become $a - n - b + n$, which is $a - b$ once more.

We can show the type of alterations allowed in addition and subtraction as follows. Let's have an upward pointing arrow indicate a particular increase in a number and a downward pointing arrow indicate a decrease. In addition, then:

$$\uparrow a + \downarrow b = a + b$$
$$\downarrow a + \uparrow b = a + b$$

In subtraction, on the other hand,

$$\uparrow a - \uparrow b = a - b$$
$$\downarrow a - \downarrow b = a - b$$

Now let's go back to our example $61 - 48$. If we add 2 to 48 to make it 50, we must also add 2 to 61 and make it 63, if we are to keep the difference unchanged. Instead of $61 - 48$, then, we have $63 - 50$, and the answer is 13 at a glance. No borrowing or carrying is necessary.

This can be done for more complicated cases, too. If you are trying to get the answer to $412 - 279$, you can first add 1 to both numbers and make it $413 - 280$; that changes a 9 in the subtrahend to a 0. Then add 20 to both numbers and it becomes $433 - 300$, which changes the 8 in the subtrahend to a 0. As for $433 - 300$, the answer is obviously 133.

With practice, you can learn to do this sort of thing at a glance. You might feel, of course, that with really long numbers it would be so difficult to add numbers little by little that it would really be easier to do it by borrowing and carrying. There you may be right but, once again, it is the small subtractions you will be meeting with day after day. Once you are handy with those, perhaps 90 per cent of your subtraction problems will trouble you no more.

CHECKING SUBTRACTION

Subtraction cannot be checked in quite the same fashion that addition can be, for in subtraction we cannot change the order of the numbers to suit ourselves. The expression $a - b$ is not equal to $b - a$. However, as I have pointed out several times in this chapter, subtraction is the reverse of addition. If we start with the problem $a - b = c$; we are justified in turning it about and saying $c + b = a$. In any correctly worked out subtraction, in other words, the difference plus the subtrahend should equal the minuend.

Consider the following subtraction:

$$
\begin{array}{r}
75,413 \\
- \ 6,295 \\
\hline
69,118
\end{array}
$$

To check the correctness of the result by simply repeating the subtraction lays you open to the possibility of repeating your mistake, whatever it was. Instead, we can check it by turning it into an addition:

$$
\begin{array}{r}
69,118 \\
+ \ 6,295 \\
\hline
75,413
\end{array}
$$

If the sum in the second calculation is not equal to the minuend in the first, then something is wrong. Naturally, it is not necessary to rewrite the problem; I do that here only to make it quite clear. The difference and the subtrahend in the problem as originally written can be added upward mentally.

Casting out nines can work for subtraction also, though in subtraction it is not likely to be as useful as in addition. Casting out nines is most useful in addition when a long series of numbers is being added, but in subtraction, we are rarely faced with more than two numbers, a minuend and a subtrahend. It is about as easy to add upward as to cast out nines. Neverthe‑less, let's consider the previous subtraction once more.

$$
\begin{array}{cc}
75{,}413 & 2 \\
-\ 6{,}295 & -4 \\
\hline
69{,}118 & 7 \\
\end{array}
$$

In the minuend, casting out $5 + 4$, we are left with $7 + 1 + 3 = 11$, and $1 + 1 = 2$. In the subtrahend, casting out 9, we have $6 + 2 + 5 = 13$ and $1 + 3 = 4$. In the difference, casting out 9 and $1 + 8$, we have $6 + 1 = 7$.

If we concentrate on the digit sums, then, we find that $2 - 4 = 7$. Is that correct? In the first place, we are subtracting a larger number from a smaller and, in this book at least, we shall not attempt such a task. Therefore we must revise the situation to make the minuend larger. We know that adding and subtracting 9's makes no difference in manipulating digit sums. Let's, therefore, add a 9 to the minuend digit sum; so that $2 + 9 = 11$. Leave it as 11, without adding the digits together so as to keep the new minuend larger than the subtrahend. Now we have $11 - 4 = 7$, which is certainly correct.

On the other hand, it is not necessary to do this, either, if we prefer not to. If we are faced with the digit-sum subtraction $2 - 4 = 7$, we need only remember that every subtraction can be reversed into an addition. We have $7 + 4 = 2$. Since $7 + 4 = 11$ and $1 + 1 = 2$, we can conclude that the subtraction is very probably correct. If the digit-sum manipulations had *not* worked out, we would have been certain there was a mistake in the subtraction.

4

Multiplication

I think it would be generally agreed that addition and subtraction are the simplest of the arithmetical operations. Even without time-saving devices, most people would accept them without much trouble. Multiplication, however, is considerably harder and more tedious; mistakes are easier to make; and most people hesitate more over working out particular problems.

Yet multiplication is only a form of addition, and is itself a kind of shortcut.

Thus, let's consider the multiplication problem 9 times 8, or to use the "multiplication sign" ($\times$), 9×8. The number 9 is the "multiplicand" in this case (from a Latin word meaning "that which is to be multiplied") while the number 8 is the "multiplier." As you all surely know, $9 \times 8 = 72$, and 72 is the "product."

But what is there in $9 \times 8 = 72$ that makes the problem a kind of addition? Remember that you can read 9×8 as "nine times eight." You are asked to take 8 "nine times." Well, if you take nine 8's and add them together: $8 + 8 + 8 + 8 + 8 + 8 + 8 + 8 + 8$, you do indeed get 72.

Because multiplication is a form of addition, it shares some of the properties of addition. Just as $a + b = b + a$, so $a \times b = b \times a$. (In algebra, the multiplication sign is generally omitted, so we can express the last statement as $ab = ba$.) Consequently if $9 \times 8 = 72$, then $8 \times 9 = 72$. Sure enough, if you add eight 9's together: $9 + 9 + 9 + 9 + 9 + 9 + 9 + 9$, the sum there too comes to 72.

The fact that multiplication is a shortcut for at least some problems in addition is at once plain. It is easier to memorize that $8 \times 9 = 72$ than to have to add all those 9's and 8's.

In the third grade or so we are usually set to memorizing the "multiplication table," a table which gives the products of all possible combinations of single digits. As a result, it soon becomes second nature for us to say $3 \times 2 = 6$, $7 \times 7 = 49$, $5 \times 9 = 45$, and so forth. We ought to be able to rattle off any combination from $0 \times 0 = 0$ to $9 \times 9 = 81$.

The multiplication table I learned as a child ran all the way up through 12, so that I also learned that $8 \times 11 = 88$, $11 \times 12 = 132$, and $12 \times 12 = 144$. It might not be a bad idea for people who want to make multiplication easier for themselves to memorize all the combinations up to 20 so that they can say, at the drop of a hat, $6 \times 15 = 90$, $17 \times 12 = 204$, $18 \times 19 = 342$, and $20 \times 20 = 400$. However, these extra memorizations, involving two-digit numbers, though handy, are not absolutely necessary. You can make out perfectly well if you memorize a multiplication table that takes you only to 9×9.

The simplest part of multiplication involves zero. Any number at all, no matter how large, when multiplied by zero gives zero as the product. We can say that $2 \times 0 = 0$; $75 \times 0 = 0$; $6,354,876 \times 0 = 0$. And, of course, $0 \times 0 = 0$.

This behavior of zero simplifies certain types of multiplication problems. Suppose, for instance, you want to multiply 10 by 10 and that you decide to do it by the step-by-step method you were taught in school. First, you multiply 10 by 0, writing down the answer; then you multiply 10 by 1, indenting the second answer; finally you add the two answers. I am sure that you all know how to do this and, in fact, that you do this sort of thing every time you multiply. The problem 10×10 would then be worked out as follows:

$$
\begin{array}{r}
10 \\
\times\ 10 \\
\hline
00 \\
10 \\
\hline
100
\end{array}
$$

The numbers that lie between the two horizontal lines are called "partial products." Notice that the first partial product comes out 00, because that partial product is the result of multiplying 10 by 0, and all multiplica-

tions by 0 yield 0. We might write 00 or 000 or even
000000000000, but all numbers made up only of zeros
are equal to 0.

We get these zeros as partial products whenever there
is a zero as one of the digits in the multiplier. Let's
take some more cases of multiplications involving numbers made up of a 1 followed by several zeros.

```
            100                    1,000
    ×       100              ×         10
    ───────────              ──────────────
            000                    0 000
          0 00                   10 00
         10 0                  ──────────────
    ───────────                   10,000
         10,000
```

In short, $100 \times 100 = 10,000$ and $1000 \times 10 = 10,000$.
If we stick to numbers of this type and study the
answers, we find that the product contains as many
zeros as do the multiplicand and multiplier put together.

In multiplying 10×10, multiplicand and multiplier
end in one zero apiece and the product 100 ends in two
zeros. In multiplying 100×100, multiplicand and multiplier end in two zeros apiece and the product, 10,000,
ends in four zeros. Again, in multiplying 1000×10, the
total number of zeros in multiplicand and multiplier is
four and the product is also 10,000.

Without bothering to multiply out in full, you can tell
that $10,000 \times 1,000$, with a total of seven zeros, must
have a product of 10,000,000.

If the numbers being multiplied contain but a single digit before the various zeros and one or both of these digits is not 1, things are hardly any more complicated. Suppose that we wish to multiply 300 by 500. We can write 300 as 3×100 and 500 as 5×100. This means that $300 \times 500 = 3 \times 100 \times 5 \times 100$. But we know from the multiplication table that $3 \times 5 = 15$ and we know from adding zeros that $100 \times 100 = 10,000$. Therefore $3 \times 100 \times 5 \times 100 = 15 \times 10,000$, or 150,000.

If you consider this preceding paragraph carefully, you see that what we are doing is to add the zeros of multiplicand and multiplier and put the product of the non-zero digits in front of the sum of those zeros.

In multiplying 300×500 we could, without ado, count zeros and see that the answer must end in four zeros, 0000. We then multiply 3×5 and place the product, 15, in front of the four zeros. That gives us our complete answer, 150,000.

Using this system, you can see quickly that 700×4000 has an answer in which 28 (that is, 7×4) is followed by five zeros. Therefore $700 \times 4000 = 2,800,000$. In the same way 5×50 has as its product 25 followed by a single zero, or 250; $100 \times 80 = 8000$; $20 \times 60 = 1200$, and so on.

Sometimes it is possible to have more zeros in the product than you might expect from merely counting the zeros in multiplicand and multiplier. Suppose you were multiplying 40×50. You know the answer will end in two zeros, 00, and that these will be preceded by the product of 4 × 5, which is 20. Therefore, 40 × 50 = 2000, which, as it turns out, ends in three zeros, not in two. The third zero, however, was added by way of the product of 4 × 5, and not by adding the zeros in multiplicand and multiplier.

This is not a matter of concern, of course. The method of counting zeros and putting the product of the single digits before those zeros will give the correct answer in any case. If an additional zero is needed, it will be added automatically.

What we see, then, is that we have learned more from the multiplication table than we perhaps supposed. In memorizing the product of 8 × 9 as 72, we also made it possible for ourselves to tell, at a glance, the product of 80 × 9, of 8 × 90, of 80 × 90, of 8000 × 900, and so on.

BEYOND THE MULTIPLICATION TABLE

But if we think that's all there is to multiplication, we are living in a fool's paradise. What if one of the numbers contains more than one digit that is not zero? What if it is not the product of 8 × 9 that we want but the product of 83 × 9?

This is something we haven't memorized in any multiplication table. Instead, we usually work it out digit by digit in the manner taught us in school. First, we multiply the 3 by the 9, which gives us 27. We put down 7 and carry 2. Then we multiply 8 × 9, which gives us 72. Adding the 2 we have carried, gives us the sum of 74. Writing this down before the 7 we had previously written down, the answer is 747. This system of multiplying without actually writing down the partial products is "short multiplication." If we multiply 83 × 9 by short multiplication, it would look like this:

$$
\begin{array}{r}
83 \\
\times \quad 9 \\
{\scriptstyle 2} \\
\hline
747
\end{array}
$$

If we wrote out the partial products in full, we would have "long multiplication," thus:

$$
\begin{array}{r}
83 \\
\times \quad 9 \\
\hline
27 \\
72 \\
\hline
747
\end{array}
$$

Is there any way of simplifying this? Yes, there is, if we follow our basic principle of changing a difficult problem into an easy one. We have already decided that once the multiplication table is memorized it is easy to multiply numbers that consist of only single digits, plus zeros. How, then, can we convert 83 into such numbers? The logical way is to write 83 as 80 + 3. The number 3 is a single digit, and the number 80 is a single digit plus a zero.

But how can one multiply 80 + 3 by 9?

Using algebraic symbolism we are multiplying a sum $a + b$ by a number c and this is written $(a + b)c$. If we clear parentheses, we find that $(a + b)c = ac + bc$. In other words, to multiply $80 + 3$ by 9, we first multiply 80×9, then 3×9, then add the two products.

This may strike you as a step backward. How can we make a multiplication simpler by changing it into two multiplications? Are we not just making it harder? Not at all. We are converting one difficult multiplication into two easy ones, and this is a step forward, not backward. We know at a glance that $80 \times 9 = 720$, and that $3 \times 9 = 27$. Since $720 + 27 = 747$, there is our answer.

You can do this in your head without trouble, in all likelihood, but if you want to do it on paper it would look like this:

$$
\begin{array}{r}
80 + 3 \\
\times\, 9 \\
\hline
720 + 27 = 747
\end{array}
$$

Naturally you can use this method on numbers involving final zeros. If you are faced with the multiplication 83×90, work out 83×9 and add the zero. Since you know that $83 \times 9 = 747$, then $83 \times 90 = 7470$. Furthermore, $830 \times 9 = 7470$ also; $8300 \times 900 = 7,470,000$, and so on.

Now let's look back a bit to the point where I multiplied 83×9 by the usual method of long multiplication. The partial products were:

$$\begin{array}{r} 27 \\ 72 \\ \hline \end{array}$$

The indented 72 might just as well have a zero after it, for that would not change things. In that case we would have:

$$\begin{array}{r} 83 \\ \times\ \ 9 \\ \hline 27 \\ 720 \\ \hline 747 \end{array}$$

This means that in ordinary long multiplication we are adding 27 and 720 to get 747, while in the method I recommend, we are adding 720 and 27. Since we are doing the same thing either way, why should one method be preferable to the other?

The answer is this: the school method works from right to left. This is to simplify the written work. Any number you write down will not have to be changed as a result of any number that you will later carry (just as in addition). The trouble is that we think of numbers from left to right, no matter how much we may work with them from right to left, and that makes for confusion.

If we try to multiply 83×9 mentally, in the usual manner, we begin by saying $3 \times 9 = 27$, put down 7 and carry 2, but since we think of 27 as "two-seven" we might carelessly put down 2 and carry 7. We then end with a completely wrong answer.

In the left-to-right method, however, we are thinking of numbers in the customary left-to-right way. We say $(80 + 3) \times 9 = 720 + 27 = 747$. It may not be any easier arithmetically, but it is certainly easier psychologically.

In the same way you can say $44 \times 6 = (40 + 4) \times 6 = 240 + 24 = 264$; and $46 \times 7 = (40 + 6) \times 7 = 280 + 42 = 322$; and so on.

Furthermore, the left-to-right method is more versatile in that it allows subtractions as well as additions. The school method of right-to-left does not allow this.

Suppose that we must multiply 89×7. We can write this $(80 + 9) \times 7 = 560 + 63 = 623$. However, adding 560 and 63 mentally might produce a bit of hesitation. Why not, then, consider 89 to be $90 - 1$, rather than $80 + 9$? Now we can say that $89 \times 7 = (90 - 1) \times 7 = 630 - 7 = 623$.

Most people would find it easier to deal with $630 - 7$ than with $560 + 63$, and the left-to-right method allows such people to make the necessary shift from addition to subtraction.

In the same way, $49 \times 8 = (50 - 1) \times 8 = 400 - 8 = 392$. And $38 \times 3 = (40 - 2) \times 3 = 120 - 6 = 114$.

Of course, you can pass this system on to numbers with more than two digits. The problem 546×6 can be expressed as $(500 + 40 + 6) \times 6 = 3000 + 240 + 36 = 3276$. Or, $329 \times 5 = (300 + 30 - 1) \times 5 = 1500 + 150 - 5 = 1645$.

If you try this technique on larger numbers, you may well find it difficult to keep all the partial products in your head while trying to sum them. Enough practice will make it easier to do so but if you would rather not devote the necessary time to such practice, all is not yet lost. You can use pencil and paper after all.

In multiplying 7625×7, you can mentally break up 7625 into $7000 + 600 + 20 + 5$, and multiply each of these portions by 7. You then write down the partial products only:

$$
\begin{array}{r}
49,000 \\
4,200 \\
140 \\
\underline{35} \\
53,375
\end{array}
$$

You may still find this faster than the usual method taught in school.

MAKING THE MULTIPLIER A SUM

So far, all the multiplications I have discussed have involved at least one number that consisted of a single digit (plus one or more zeros, on occasion). What if both numbers in a multiplication have at least two digits other than zero? What if we wanted to multiply 48×16?

There are a number of ways of tackling such a problem. The first that might occur to you is to break up both numbers into single-digit numbers, with or with-

out zeros. The number 48 can be written $40 + 8$ and
the number 16 can be written $10 + 6$. But once that is
done, how do we go about multiplying $40 + 8$ by
$10 + 6$?

In algebraic notation, we are asking how one multiplies $(a + b) c + d)$. The answer is $ac + ad + bc +$
bd. In other words, each part of the first sum must
be multiplied in turn by each part of the last sum. Then
all the multiples must be added together.

In the case of 48×16, we might write matters out
in full as follows:

The arrows show the combinations we must multiply.
(In fact, the crossed arrows in the center are thought by
some people to have given rise to the symbol $\times$ for multiplication. This method, in all likelihood, was used in
ancient times quite often.)

If we carry out the four multiplications indicated by
the arrows, we have $40 \times 10 = 400$, $40 \times 6 = 240$, $8 \times$
$10 = 80$, and $8 \times 6 = 48$. We then add $400 + 240 +$
$80 + 48$ and get 768 as the answer. It doesn't matter in
which order we do the multiplications or in which order
we add the multiples. The answer will always be 768.

Until you have considerable practice you won't find
this particularly easy. You have to remember four numbers and add them in your head. If you multiply a

three-digit number by a two-digit number, as in 752×34, you have to remember six partial products. The multiplication can be written $(700 + 50 + 2) \times (30 + 4)$. If we multiply each of the numbers in the first parenthesis by each of the numbers in the second, we get the following list of partial products: $21,000 + 2800 + 1500 + 200 + 60 + 8$ and that equals $25,568$. If you multiply a three-digit number by a three-digit number, you will have nine partial products to remember (or to write down.)

This system works, but it is not a good example of quick and easy math. What we must look for, then, is a simpler method. We might find one, perhaps, which wouldn't work in every single case, but which would work in certain cases, at least. Well, that's better than nothing.

Consider that next to multiplying by 0 the easiest form of multiplication is that of multiplying by 1. Any number multiplied by 1 remains itself. This means that $56 \times 1 = 56$ and, remembering our zero rule, $56 \times 10 = 560$, $56 \times 100 = 5600$, and so on.

Suppose, then, that we can break up the multiplier into the sum of two or more numbers, each of which involves only a single 1, plus one or more zeros. For example, if we are multiplying a number by 11, we can express the 11 as $10 + 1$. We then multiply the number first by 10, then by 1, and add the multiples. But it is so simple to multiply by 10 or by 1, that we don't have to break up the other number at all.

For instance, 54×11 is equal to $54 \times (10 + 1)$ or 54×10 plus 54×1. You can see at a glance that this is $540 + 54 = 594$. In the same way $62 \times 11 = 620 + 62 = 682$. We have here the case of the multiplication of a two-digit number by a two digit-number where only two multiples, not four, need be added. Furthermore, the two multiples are closely related, differing only by a zero, which makes matters all the better.

This same device will work for even larger numbers, so that $322 \times 11 = 3220 + 322 = 3542$. For the larger numbers you may want a piece of paper to jot down the partial products.

Sometimes you will read the following rule offered for the multiplication of a two-digit number by 11: add the two digits and place the sum between them. Thus, $5 + 4 = 9$, so $54 \times 11 = 594$; $3 + 6 = 9$, so $36 \times 11 = 396$; $6 + 2 = 8$, so $62 \times 11 = 682$. This is all right as far as it goes, but it only works for pairs of digits that do not add up to more than 9.

Suppose that you wanted to multiply 75×11. The sum of 7 and 5 is 12. Someone who follows rules without understanding them may say that $75 \times 11 = 7125$ and be quite wrong. If, instead, he remembers that 11 may be expressed as $10 + 1$, he will decide that $75 \times 11 = 750 + 75 = 825$. That is the correct answer.

Of course, since 11 is the simplest two-digit number that does not contain zero, you may think that the ability to multiply quickly by 11 is not much of a victory. Think of the method, however, as representing a general principle. If it works for 11, it will work for 101, or 1001, or 10,001.

We can break 101 into $100 + 1$. Then 62×101 becomes $(62 \times 100) + (62 \times 1)$, or $6200 + 62$ or 6262. And 403×101 is equal to $40,300 + 403$, or 40,703. You can see for yourself how to multiply by 1001, 10,001, and other numbers of this type.

Or, for that matter, suppose that you want to multiply by 111. This breaks up into $100 + 10 + 1$. Now, then, 68×111 is equal to $6800 + 680 + 68$, or 7548.

Where only 1's and 0's are involved in the original number, the school method of multiplication is not very difficult, to be sure, and converting the multiplier into a sum does not save much time. However, the principle, once understood, can be used for numbers that contain neither a 1 nor a 0, provided subtraction rather than addition is used.

Suppose you wanted to multiply 7249×9. The usual method is to say that $9 \times 9 = 81$, put down 1 and carry 8; $4 \times 9 = 36$, plus 8 is 44, put down 4 and carry 4; and so on. But suppose we look upon 9 as equal to $10 - 1$. That means that $7249 \times 9 = 7249 \times (10 - 1) = (7249 \times 10) - (7249 \times 1) = 72,490 - 7249 = 65,241$. You'll want to use paper and pencil, perhaps to make the subtraction, but even so that would be much quicker than the multiplication. All you ever do is add a zero to the number and subtract the number itself. Thus, $11,476 \times 9 = 114,760 - 11,476 = 103,284$.

This device of changing a multiplier into a difference

rather than a sum is even handier when that multiplier is 99. If you are trying to multiply 48 × 99 and want to avoid long multiplication, your first thought might be to convert 99 into a sum 90 + 9. This means you have to multiply 48 first by 90, then by 9. Actually, you need multiply 48 by 9 only. This comes to 432. Multiplying 48 by 90 gives the same product with a 0 added: 4320. Adding, 4320 + 432 = 4752. This is easier than long multiplication, but perhaps not very much easier.

Suppose you reverse the multiplication and make it 99 × (40 + 8), breaking up the 48 into a sum. This strikes me as still harder. Thus, 99 × 4 = 396 and 99 × 40 = 3960. Again 99 × 8 = 792. Finally, 3960 + 792 = 4752.

But suppose that you decide to change 99 into a difference and make it 100 − 1. Now 48 × 99 becomes 48 × (100 − 1) or (48 × 100) − (48 × 1), or 4800 − 48, or 4752. I think you will agree that this is by far the easiest of the three possible shortcuts.

It is important to realize, by the way, that there are no hard and fast rules for handling an arithmetical operation. There is usually a variety of routes you can take to the correct answer. Sometimes as in the case I've just given, one route is so much simpler than others you might think of that there is no question in your mind as to which to take. Anytime you must multiply by 99, you will automatically consider it as 100 − 1.

Sometimes there may be some doubt. Consider the following: 72 × 9. You might say to yourself that one should obviously treat 9 as $10 - 1$. The answer would then be $72 \times (10 - 1)$ or $720 - 72 = 648$. On the other hand, it might have occurred to you to write 72 as $70 + 2$. The problem then becomes $(70 + 2) \times 9 = 630 + 18 = 648$.

In the first alternative it is childishly easy to multiply by 10 and 1; but the subtraction $720 - 72$ requires a little thought. In the second alternative, multiplying by 9 isn't quite as easy as multiplying by either 10 or 1. However, the partial products yield an addition, $630 + 18$, which is very simple. Which alternative ought you to use?

I don't think there is any hard and fast decision here. Use the alternative with which you are most comfortable. Each person has his own way of thinking, his own mental comforts and dislikes. One person might not mind a difficult subtraction if he can avoid multiplying by 9, while another isn't the least bothered by multiplication by 9, provided he can avoid a subtraction that involves carrying.

Suit yourself.

Changing a multiplier into a sum or difference involving a 1 can be useful even for numbers that are not near the very simple 10, 100, or 1,000 point. If you wish, for instance, to multiply 34×61, you might note that $61 = 60 + 1$. Multiplying 34×60 can be carried through by multiplying 34×6 and adding a zero. Since $34 \times 6 = 204$, then $34 \times 60 = 2040$. Now we must add to that 34×1, which is, of course, 34. So $2040 + 34 = 2074$.

More startling, you can multiply 34×59 without trouble (even in your head, if you choose), if you consider $59 = 60 - 1$. The problem becomes $34 \times (60 - 1) = 2040 - 34 = 2006$.

DOUBLING

Next to multiplying by 1 and by 0, it is easiest to multiply by 2. We have more occasion to multiply by 2 (that is, to double a number) than to multiply by any number higher than 2. Furthermore, as youngsters we early learn to double numbers. Almost the first additions children learn actually are doublings.

"One and one is two," they will come home, chanting, "two and two is four; three and three is six." Obviously, the sum of any number with itself is equal to double that number, or to that number multiplied by 2. In algebraic notation, $n + n = 2n = n \times 2$.

As a result of such early training, we can double even a large number without trouble and can do so despite the fact that this might involve carrying. Most of us can say $36 \times 2 = 72$ or $49 \times 2 = 98$ or even $274 \times 2 = 548$ rapidly and without batting an eye.

This means that it should be fairly easy to multiply any two-digit number (and sometimes larger ones) by 12, if we consider 12 as equal to $10 + 2$. To multiply a number by 10, we just add a zero; to multiply by 2 we just double; and then we add the two results. Thus $34 \times 12 = 34 \times (10 + 2) = 340 + 68 = 408$; and $81 \times$

$12 = 810 + 162 = 972$. For that matter, $432 \times 12 = 4320 + 864 = 5184$.

In the same way, provided that we switch to subtraction, we can multiply by 98, which we can represent as $100 - 2$. We can then say that $34 \times 98 = 34 \times (100 - 2) = 3400 - 68 = 3332$.

Other combinations are possible, too. If the multiplier is 21, that can be expressed as $20 + 1$. To multiply by 20 we need only double and add a zero. Hence $52 \times 21 = 52 \times (20 + 1) = 1040 + 52 = 1092$. As for 19, that is $20 - 1$. Therefore, $64 \times 19 = 64 \times (20 - 1) = 1280 - 64 = 1216$.

Doubling (or multiplying by 2) is so much simpler than multiplying by any number higher than 2 that we ought to make use of it whenever we can. Sometimes doing this enables us to multiply by numbers that would otherwise be tricky to handle.

Consider the number 16 as multiplier. If we wish to represent it as a sum or a difference, we can write it as $10 + 6$ or as $20 - 4$. If we do this we are involved with multiplication by 10 or by 20, which is easy, but also with multiplication by 6 or by 4, which is less easy.

Thus, 72×16 will become $72 \times (10 + 6) = 720 + 432 = 1152$. Or $72 \times 16 = 72 \times (20 - 4) = 1440 - 288 = 1152$. Neither alternative is very easy. Is there any way in which we can do better?

Let's consider first if we must write multipliers only as sums and differences. Can they be represented as products? For instance, 12 is not only $10 + 2$, it is also 4×3. If we are faced with 34×12, we might decide to tackle it as $34 \times (10 + 2)$, but might we not also consider it to be $34 \times (4 \times 3)$? We know how to handle the former, but how do we handle the other?

It turns out that if we multiply a number by 4, then multiply the product by 3, we get the same answer as we would have gotten if we multiplied the original number by 12. (In algebraic notation, if $bc = d$, then $abc = ad$.) This means that we can always write an inconvenient multiplier as the product of two smaller numbers and then multiply by first one and then the other. It may well be that multiplying twice by small numbers would be easier than multiplying once by a large number.

Thus, 34×12 becomes $34 \times 4 \times 3$. First $34 \times 4 = 136$; then $136 \times 3 = 408$.

This probably strikes you as not much of an improvement and certainly not so easy as saying $34 \times 12 = 34 \times (10 + 2) = 340 + 68 = 408$. But we must not conclude from this that multipliers ought always to be considered as sums or differences and never as products.

Consider 16 again, where we have decided that using it as either $10 + 6$ or $20 - 4$ does not make matters particularly easy. What if, instead, we considered 16 to be $2 \times 2 \times 2 \times 2$? In that case, if we wanted to multiply a number by 16, we could multiply it by 2, multiply the product by 2, multiply that product by 2, and multiply that product by 2. In other words, we would double the original number four successive times. Doubling is so easy that four doublings might well be done more quickly than a single multiplication by 16. If we want to solve 23 × 16, we can double 23 to 46, double again to 92, double a third time to 184, and double a fourth time to 368.

If we wish, we can, without trouble, double 368 to 736 and get the answer to 23 × 32 (since 32 is 16 × 2). Another doubling brings us to 1472, which is 23 × 64, and still another doubling yields 2944, which is 23 × 128.

We can summarize this as follows:

> One doubling is multiplication by 2.
> Two doublings is multiplication by 4.
> Three doublings is multiplication by 8.
> Four doublings is multiplication by 16.
> Five doublings is multiplication by 32.
> Six doublings is multiplication by 64.
> Seven doublings is multiplication by 128.

You can continue this as far as you like, but it is the small numbers as multipliers that are most useful.

Nor need you work only with doubles of 2 itself. You can double and redouble any answer you have obtained by a multiplication according to some other method. Let's go back to 34 × 12, where we wrote 12 as 4 × 3 and found the results not entirely satisfactory. But, as I have already shown, it is not necessary to write a multiplier as the product of two numbers, it can be the product of any number of numbers. Thus, 12 can not only be written as 4×3 but also as $2 \times 2 \times 3$. Therefore $34 \times 12 = 34 \times 2 \times 2 \times 3$.

Now it makes sense when we are multiplying a number by a series of multipliers to make use of the largest multiplier first. As we multiply, the original number will get larger and larger, and if we take care of the largest multiplier first, that will be done while the original number is at its smallest.

If we say $34 \times 2 \times 2 \times 3$, we double 34 twice, first to 68 next to 136, and we must then solve 136×3.

If, on the other hand, we write the problem $34 \times 3 \times 2 \times 2$, it is only 34 that we must multiply by 3 and that is simple, for the answer is 102, as you can see quickly. Now we have $102 \times 2 \times 2$, and doubling it twice we have first 204 then 408. You will agree, I think, that it is almost as easy to work out 34×12 by considering it to be $34 \times 3 \times 2 \times 2$ as it would be to work it out as $34 \times (10 + 2)$.

Again, take 13×28. You can express 28 as $7 \times 2 \times 2$, the largest multiple being placed first. Therefore $13 \times 28 = 13 \times 7 \times 2 \times 2$. It may be that you remember that $13 \times 7 = 91$ because you have memorized the multiplication table up to 20×20. Or perhaps you see that $13 \times 7 = (10 + 3) \times 7 = 70 + 21 = 91$. In either case, you see that $13 \times 7 \times 2 \times 2 = 91 \times 2 \times 2$. You need simply double 91 twice, first to 182, then to 364, and that is your answer: $13 \times 28 = 364$.

Remember, though, that you are not condemned to one particular line of attack. It may be actually simpler not to write a multiplier as the product of a number of small multiples. Suppose we are dealing with 35×24. we can write 24 as $3 \times 2 \times 2 \times 2$. Therefore $35 \times 24 = 35 \times 3 \times 2 \times 2 \times 2$. First $35 \times 3 = 105$, and if we double that three times (first to 210, then to 420, and finally to 840), we can conclude that $35 \times 24 = 840$.

But we can also consider 24 as 12×2. That means $35 \times 24 = 35 \times 12 \times 2$. As for 35×12, we can see at a glance that it is equal to $35 \times (10 + 2) = 350 + 70 = 420$. We need double that only once to 840, and there is the answer again. You might well consider this second alternative the easier of the two. I think I would myself. Incidentally, doubling 840 to 1680 and then to 3360, shows us that $35 \times 48 = 1680$ and that $35 \times 96 = 3360$.

Another example of alternate methods arises if we are going to multiply 71×22, for instance. You might decide that 22 can be considered as 11×2. Therefore $71 \times 22 = 71 \times 11 \times 2$. It is easy to see that 71×11 equals $710 + 71 = 781$, and doubling that gives us 1562 as our answer: $71 \times 22 = 1562$.

On the other hand, we might say that $71 \times 22 = 71 \times (20 + 2) = 1420 + 142 = 1562$. Suit yourself.

CHECKING MULTIPLICATION

Since multiplication is a form of addition, it is not surprising that the methods of checking that apply to addition also apply to multiplication.

For instance, if we perform addition of a series of

numbers downward, we can easily check the answer if
we perform the same addition upward. This can be
done in multiplication also. Consider the following
multiplication:

$$
\begin{array}{r}
75,812 \\
\times \quad 2,749 \\
\hline
682\ 308 \\
3\ 032\ 48 \\
53\ 048\ 4 \\
151\ 624 \\
\hline
208,387,188
\end{array}
$$

It looks pretty, but is it correct? You might check by
repeating the multiplication a second time, following
exactly in the footsteps of the first; but if you have made
a mistake there is a reasonable chance that you will repeat it. It would be better if you repeat the multiplication reversing, this time, the position of the multiplicand
and multiplier. This gives you:

$$
\begin{array}{r}
2,749 \\
\times \quad 75,812 \\
\hline
5\ 498 \\
27\ 49 \\
2\ 199\ 2 \\
13\ 745 \\
192\ 43 \\
\hline
208,407,188
\end{array}
$$

The answers do not check. The product is 208,387,188
in the first multiplication and 208,407,188 in the sec-

ond. In one or the other, a mistake has been made. It is necessary to go over both to see which answer is the correct one. (Perhaps neither is correct.) If the two products had come out the same, we might have been reasonably certain that no mistake was involved.

Here is where casting out nines comes into its own as a checking process. It is much more useful in multiplication than in addition. A multiplication problem usually takes up a considerably longer time than an addition problem, so that it is much more time-consuming to check by repeating the problem with the numbers rearranged. Casting out nines, however, takes no more time in multiplication than in addition.

In multiplication, only the multiplicand, multiplier, and product need be involved in casting out nines, and we need not worry about the partial products. We can write the first multiplication simply like this:

$$
\begin{array}{rr}
75,812 & 5 \\
\times \quad 2,749 & 4 \\
\hline
208,387,188 & 0
\end{array}
$$

In the multiplicand, 75,812, we can cast out $7 + 2$ and $8 + 1$, leaving only the 5 as the digit sum. In the multiplier, 2749, we can cast out the $2 + 7$ and the 9, leaving only the 4 as the digit sum. In the product, 208,387,188, we can cast out $2 + 7$ and $1 + 8$, leaving $8 + 3 + 8 + 8 = 27$. But $2 + 7$ can be cast out so that the digit sum of the product is 0.

Here the digit sums must be manipulated as in multiplication, of course, and we must say that $5 \times 4 = 20$ and $2 + 0 = 2$. Therefore $5 \times 4 = 2$ and 5×4 does *not* equal zero. There is, therefore, a mistake in the multiplication above.

Let's try the other one:

$$
\begin{array}{rc}
2,749 & 4 \\
\times\ 75,812 & 5 \\
\hline
208,407,188 & 2 \\
\end{array}
$$

The numbers 2749 and 75,812 have the digit sums of 4 and 5 respectively, as before. The new product, 208,407,188, can be simplified by casting out $2 + 7$ and $1 + 8$, and now, ignoring the zeros, we sum the digits $8 + 4 + 8 = 20$ and $2 + 0 = 2$. As far as the digit sums are concerned, we have $4 \times 5 = 2$. But $4 \times 5 = 20$ and $2 + 0 = 2$. The digit-sum manipulation is a correct one and the answer is in all likelihood correct. (I will leave it to the reader to see where the exact mistake is in the first multiplication.)

5

Division

JUST as subtraction is the reverse of addition, so division is the reverse of multiplication. Since we know that $5 \times 3 = 15$, we can turn that about, replace the multiplication sign by a division sign ($\div$), and say that $15 \div 3 = 5$.

Also, since $5 \times 3 = 3 \times 5$, we can say that $3 \times 5 = 15$, too. In that case $15 \div 5 = 3$.

(In algebraic terminology, we can say that if $a \times b = c$, then $c \div b = a$ and $c \div a = b$. In algebra, as I said earlier in the book, multiplication signs are omitted. Then, too, division is usually indicated by putting the two symbols involved in division in the form of a fraction. We can therefore say that if $ab = c$, then $c/a = b$ and $c/b = a$).

In the example $15 \div 3 = 5$, the first number, 15, is the "dividend" (from a Latin word meaning "that which is to be divided"). The number 3, which does the dividing, is, naturally, the "divisor," while the number 5, which is the answer to the problem, is the "quotient." "Quotient" is from a Latin word meaning "how many times?" I suppose it was customary for teachers to ask "How many times does 3 go into 15?" The answer to "how many times?" is, obviously, the quotient.

Just as multiplication shares some of the properties of addition, so division shares some of the properties of subtraction. In addition and multiplication it does not matter how you arrange the numbers being added or multiplied: $a + b = b + a$ or $ab = ba$. In subtraction and division, however, the order of the numbers *does* matter. It is important to realize that $a - b$ is *not* equal to $b - a$, and $a \div b$ is not equal to $b \div a$.

Thus, $5 - 3 = 2$, but $3 - 5$ equals what? For a proper answer we must introduce negative numbers. Again, $15 \div 5 = 3$, but $5 \div 15$ equals what? For a proper answer here, we must introduce fractions. Therefore, if subtraction exposes us to the perils of negative numbers, division exposes us to the perils of fractions. Actually, the perils of fractions are greater than those of negative numbers. Once you have mastered a few rules, negative numbers can be handled in much the same way that positive numbers can be handled. Furthermore, it is easy to avoid negative numbers. As long as you remember to keep the minuend from being smaller than the subtrahend you will never run into negative numbers. For this reason it is possible to ignore negative numbers in grade school, and it is even possible for me to ignore them in this book.

The manipulation of fractions, unfortunately, is rather

more complicated than that of either positive or negative numbers. Even the simple addition of fractions can
be complicated, and if one deals with division, fractions
are bound to come. If the divisor is larger than the
dividend, the quotient is always a fraction. Even if we
are careful to keep the divisor from being larger than
the dividend, we can't avoid them. For example,
$16 \div 5 = 3\frac{1}{5}$ and $14 \div 5 = 2\frac{4}{5}$, and both quotients
contain fractions. In fact, very few divisions come out
"even"; very few divisions, that is, give quotients that
are whole numbers and do not contain fractions.

There is no number greater than 1 that will evenly
divide most numbers. The closest is the number 2,
which will evenly divide half the numbers you can
write. The number 3 will evenly divide only 1 out of
3 numbers; the number 4 will evenly divide only 1 out
of 4 numbers; the number 5 will evenly divide only 1
out of 5 numbers, and so forth. The larger the number
used as divisor, the fewer numbers it will go into
evenly and the more likely we are to find ourselves
with fractions.

It is for this reason that fractions cannot be avoided
in grade school as negative numbers can be. Nor can
fractions be ignored in this book, although I will do the
best I can and leave them for the final chapter.

Because fractions are more difficult to manipulate
than whole numbers, schoolchildren find them almost
always painful at first. They've managed whole num-

bers, feel pleased at having been able to do so, and now suddenly find that there is such a thing as "higher mathematics." Very often this disillusionment lasts the rest of one's life, and a fear of fractions is retained into adulthood.

This fear more than anything else worries people about division. The possibility that a division will not come out even is something that produces nervousness. There is always a certain fear that a fraction will spring out suddenly, and a certain relief when a division does come out even and no fraction appears.

It might therefore be comfortable, in doing divisions, if you could tell in advance, and with very little trouble, if the problem were to come out even or not. It would make very little difference arithmetically, but it might make a great deal of difference psychologically, and that is important.

Now let us say that if $b \div a$ gives a whole number as quotient, that b is divisible by a. In other words, 15 is divisible by 3, but 16 and 14 are not divisible by 3. What we want, then, is some easy test for "divisibility" where particular numbers are divisors. For instance, if 3 is the divisor, we need a test for divisibility by 3, so that we can tell at a glance that 15 is divisible by 3, and that 45 is, and that 75 is, but that 25 and 35 are not, and that 65 and 85 are not, either.

To seek for such tests, let's tackle the possible divisors one by one, beginning with 1. (You might think, Why not begin with 0? However, one of the most important rules in mathematics is this: never divide by 0 under any circumstances. It is not allowed! Don't even ever allow yourself to think of it!)

DIVISIBILITY BY 2, 5, AND 10

Dividing by 1 is no problem, for it leaves the number unchanged just as multiplying by 1 does. In other words, $5 \div 1 = 5$, $17 \div 1 = 17$, $365 \div 1 = 365$, and so on. All numbers are divisible by 1 and there is usually no point in even involving oneself in such a division, since no change is introduced.

The first real problem begins with 2. Now remember that I said that division was the reverse of multiplication. In other words, if $5 \times 2 = 10$, then $10 \div 2 = 5$. This means that any whole number obtained by multiplying another whole number by 2 is itself divisible by 2. Thus, $17 \times 2 = 34$ and $18 \times 2 = 36$, therefore both 34 and 36 are divisible by 2, for $34 \div 2 = 17$ and $36 \div 2 = 18$. However, 35 is not divisible by 2 because there is no whole number which, when multiplied by 2, gives 35. Try to find one.

So now we see a possible way to list all the numbers that are divisible by 2. We simply multiply all the numbers in turn by 2 and list the products:

$$0 \times 2 = 0$$
$$1 \times 2 = 2$$
$$2 \times 2 = 4$$
$$3 \times 2 = 6$$
$$4 \times 2 = 8$$
$$5 \times 2 = 10, \text{etc.}$$

But if we look at the products, we see that we have a
series of numbers that begins with 0 and adds 2, then
adds 2 again, then adds 2 again, and so on. We are
"counting by twos." We can therefore list all the numbers divisible by two, simply by continuing this counting by twos, without bothering actually to multiply.
The numbers divisible by 2 turn out to be:

0	2	4	6	8
10	12	14	16	18
20	22	24	26	28, etc.

No matter how far you continue, you will notice that
every number divisible by 2 ends with either a 0, a 2,
a 4, a 6, or an 8; or are those digits themselves. Nor is
any such number skipped. Every number ending with
0, 2, 4, 6, or 8 is included in the list, as far as you care to
carry the list. These numbers are the "even numbers"
and they are called that because they are evenly divisible by 2. We learn to tell the even numbers at quite
an early age. If I were to state the rule that all even
numbers are divisible by 2 you would have no trouble
in that respect afterward.

The digits 1, 3, 5, 7, 9 are *not* even numbers. Neither
is any larger number that ends in one of those digits.
Those numbers that are not even are "odd numbers"
and we can tell an odd number at a glance, too. All
odd numbers are *not* divisible by 2.

You will notice, by the way, that 0 is divisible by 2,
for $0 \div 2 = 0$. In fact, 0 is divisible by any number,

for $0 \div 5 = 0$; $0 \div 17 = 0$; $0 \div 562 = 0$; and so forth. However, the quotient is always 0 in these cases, so such divisions serve little purpose.

(It is important to remember that you can divide 0, but you cannot divide *by* it. Or we can put it this way: 0 can be a dividend, or a quotient, but *never* a divisor.)

The case of divisibility by 2 is so familiar to all of us that you may wonder why I have spent so much time on it. My reason for doing so is that the system I used, which is so easily understood in the case of 2, will also apply to working out rules for divisibility by other numbers. To decide what numbers are divisible by 3 or by 5 or by 18, we start with 0 and list the numbers, counting by threes, by fives or by eighteens, respectively, and see if we can find a general rule. (To be sure, we might not.)

Take 10 as an example. If we start with 0 and count by tens, we have 0, 10, 20, 30, 40, 50, 60, and so on. Every member in the list ends with a zero, and no such numbers are skipped. Therefore we can say that any number ending with a zero is divisible by 10. We can also say that any number that does *not* end with a 0 is *not* divisible by 10. This is true because in starting with 0 and counting by tens we never hit any number *but* those that end with zero.

Notice that a number ending with 0 is also an even number and therefore divisible by 2. This is perfectly all right, for there is no reason why a particular number might not be divisible by more than one divisor. For instance $20 \div 10 = 2$ and $20 \div 2 = 10$. The important point is that *all* numbers divisible by 10 are also divisible by 2, and this follows from the rules we have worked out for divisibility.

Again, try counting by hundreds: 0, 100, 200, 300, and so on. You see at once that any number ending in 00 is divisible by 100, but such a number also ends in one 0 and is therefore divisible by 10; and, of course, also by 2. You can see for yourself that any number ending in 000 is divisible by 1,000, by 100, by 10, and by 2. (It may also be divisible by other numbers, too, and in fact, is.)

Or try 5. In counting by fives, we have 0, 5, 10, 15, 20, 25, 30, 35, 40, and so on. Every number ends either in a 5 or a 0, and no such number is skipped. Therefore, any number that ends with either a 5 or a 0 is divisible by 5.

This means that any number that ends in 0 (or 00, or 000, and so on) is divisible by 5 as well as by 10 and by 2.

DIVISIBILITY BY 4 AND 8

Rules for divisibility by 2, by 5, and by 10 all share this in common: it is only necessary to look at the last digit of the number.

The rules are not quite so easy for the other digits. Consider 4, for instance. If we start with 0 and count by fours, we have:

0	4	8	12	16
20	24	28	32	36
40	44	48	52	56, etc.

Here all the numbers are even, but some of the even numbers are skipped (half of them, in fact). You go from 0 to 4, skipping 2; then you go from 4 to 8, skipping 6; then from 8 to 12, skipping 10; and so on. We can deduce two things from this. First, if a number ends in an odd digit, it is *not* divisible by 4. Second, if a number ends in an even digit, it may be divisible by 4 and it may not, the odds being fifty-fifty.

Let's go further, then. If we continue counting by fours, we will eventually reach 100 (try it and see); past that we go on to 104, 108, 112, 116, 120, 124, 128, and so on. The last two digits, as you see, repeat the original series. That will bring us to 200 and carry us forward to 204, 208, 212, etc., then to 300, 304, 308, 312, etc., then to 400, and so on. The last two digits will always be found in the original series. Therefore, if we know that 24 is divisible by 4, we also know that 524 is divisible by 4, as well as 1824, 364,024, and 999,999,924.

To test divisibility by 4, consequently, it is enough to look at the last two digits of a number (however long) and see if that is divisible by 4. You can test that by actually dividing it by 4, if you haven't memorized the series of multiples of 4 from 0 to 100.

Perhaps you hesitate at dividing by 4. If you are faced with the number 1576 and wish to know if it is divisible by 4, you have to tell whether 76 is divisible by 4, and you may find such a test not quick and easy enough. In that case, look at it this way. Since $2 \times 2 = 4$, it follows that if a number is multiplied by 2 and the product is again multiplied by 2 it is as though the original number were multiplied by 4. Since division is the reverse of multiplication, it also follows that if a number is divided by 2 and the quotient is divided again by 2 then this is as though the original number had been divided by 4.

I'll give you an example to sharpen the point. We know that $36 \div 4 = 9$. What, then, if we have 36 twice? Well, $36 \div 2 = 18$ and $18 \div 2 = 9$. The answer is 9 in either case, and this will work in any example you choose. (Algebraically we can say that $(a/b)/c = a/bc$.)

To check, then, if a number is divisible by 4, one need only see if it can be divided by 2 twice. It is much easier to divide by 2 than by 4 (simply because, as in multiplying by 2, we come up against division by 2 so much more often than any other kind of division that we automatically get more practice).

Now let us look at 1576 again. It is an even number so it may be divisible by 4. We concentrate on 76 and divide by 2 to get 38, then divide that by 2 to get 19. We were able to divide by 2 twice which means that 76 is divisible by 4 and that the whole number therefore is divisible by 4.

In fact, we don't even have to divide by 2 twice. If

the first division by 2 gives us a quotient that ends with
an even number, we know automatically that that quotient is also divisible by 2 and that the original number
is divisible by 4. On the other hand, if the first division
gives us an odd number then the quotient is not divisible by 2 and the original number, although divisible
by 2, is not divisible by 4.

The number 14,154 ends with the digits 54. On division by 2, we get 27, an odd number; hence, 14,154
is not divisible by 4. If it were 14,152, division by 2 of
the last two digits 52 would give us 26, an even number.
Hence, 14,152 is divisible by 4.

The number 8 as divisor carries matters one step
further. Let us start with 0 and count by eights:

0	8	16	24	32
40	48	56	64	72
80	88	96	104	112, etc.

Notice that you do not land evenly on 100 as you do in
the case of adding by fours. Between 100 and 200, the
last two digits are different from those we found between 0 and 100. We have 104, 112, 120, 128, 136, and
so on.

The number 200, however, is divisible by 8, and
would fall in the series if you continued it. After that,
the final digits would repeat as they were in the group
below 100. You would have 208, 216, 224, 232, and so

on. Then 300 would not fall in the series, while 400 would; 500 would not fall in the series, while 600 would, and so on.

In some groups of one hundred, certain endings would represent divisibility by 8 and in other groups other endings would. The two groups would alternate. Thus, 104, 304, 504, and 704 are divisible by 8, but 204, 404, 604, and 804 are not. Again, 232, 432, 632, and 832 are divisible by 8, but 132, 332, 532, and 732 are not.

We can set up two rules for divisibility by 8, according to whether the digits in the hundreds column is odd or even (counting 0 as even). If the hundreds digit is even, the last two digits must be divisible by 8. If the hundreds digit is odd the last two digits must be divisible by 4, but *not* by 8. And, of course, if the last two digits are not divisible by 4, you need look no further; the number is then not divisible by 8, no matter what the hundreds digit is.

However, such a double-edged rule is quite complicated, too complicated to make a quick-and-easy mathematician happy. Is there anything better?

If you continue the series of counting by 8's far enough, you will come to the number 1000, which is divisible by 8. After that you will get 1008, 1016, 1024, 1032, and so on. Then you will eventually hit 2000 and follow with 2008, 2016, and so on. You will hit 3000, 4000 and all the rest of that sort.

This means that the last three digits of any number

divisible by 8 will duplicate the series running from 0
to 1000. If those last three digits are divisible by 8 then
the whole number is divisible by 8. Since 888 is divisible by 8, the number 1888 is divisible by 8, and so
are 2888, 5888, 72,888, and 9,345,811,888.

Since $8 = 2 \times 2 \times 2$, we can check divisibility by 8
by dividing three times by 2. Suppose we have the
number 21,911. It is odd so it cannot be divisible by 8.
(Incidentally, just a point — no odd number can be
divisible by *any* even number.) How about 21,918?
It is even, so it may be. Concentrate on the last three
digits: 918. Divide by 2 and get 459. That is odd and
the process stops. What about 21,916? Well, 916 ÷
$2 = 458$ and $458 \div 2 = 229$ and the process stops. Still
no good. We must be able to divide by 2 three times.
What about 21,912? Well, $912 \div 2 = 456$; $456 \div 2 =$
228; and $228 \div 2 = 114$. The triple division by 2 is possible, so 21,912 is divisible by 8.

If a triple division strikes you as lengthy, you can
shorten the procedure but you must be prepared to
divide by 4. Remember that $8 = 4 \times 2$. That means
that a number that is divisible by 8 is divisible by 4, giving a quotient that is divisible by 2 and is hence an even
number. Consider the number 8,555,111,844. Is it divisible by 8? Take the last three digits 844 and divide
by 4. The answer is 211, an odd number. The original
number is not divisible by 8. If the number had been
8,555,111,848; we would have found that $848 \div 4 =$
212, an even number, and now the original number

would be divisible by 8. The rule is: if you can divide the last three digits by 4 and get an even number, the original number is divisible by 8.

Naturally, any number divisible by 4 is automatically divisible by 2, since if the number can be divided by 2 twice (as is necessary for divisibility by 4) it can certainly be divided by 2 once. By the same reasoning, any number divisible by 8 is also divisible by 4 and by 2.

DIVISIBILITY BY 3, 6, AND 9

When we consider 3 as a divisor, we encounter a new situation altogether. Let's start with 0 and count by threes:

0	3	6	9	12	15
18	21	24	27	30	33
36	39	42	45	48	51, etc.

At first glance, this looks hopeless. Some of the numbers are odd, some even — in fact, they alternate: odd, even, odd, even, odd, even . . . Furthermore, there are numbers that end with every possible digit from 0 to 9. If we continue the list on and on, we would find that there are numbers in the series which contain any combination of 2 digits at the end and any combination of 3 digits at the end, and so forth. (The trouble is that 100 is not divisible by 3, nor 1,000, nor 10,000, nor 100,000 — nor any number of this sort. Therefore, the series never starts over again.)

However, suppose you work with digit sums for each

of the numbers in the series formed by counting by threes. The first three numbers offer no problem. They are 0, 3, and 6, and as single digits have digit sums equal to 0, 3, and 6, respectively. Then 9, and if we follow the practice of casting out nines, the digit sum is 0.

The next number is 12, with a digit sum of 3; then 15 with a digit sum of 6; then 18 with a digit sum of 0. If we continue the series as high as we like and list the digit sums for each number, we find we will have a digit-sum series of 0, 3, 6, 0, 3, 6, 0, 3, 6, 0, 3, 6, and so on, for as long as we can manage to continue. Furthermore, the numbers that are not in the series and are therefore not divisible by 3, have digit sums that are 1, 2, 4, 5, 7, or 8 and are *never* 0, 3, or 6.

We conclude, then, that any number with a digit sum of either 0, 3, or 6 is divisible by 3. A number with any other digit sum is not divisible by 3.

Suppose that we take the number 562,789,002. We cast out the 9 and the $2 + 7$ and we find that what remains is $5 + 6 + 8 + 2 = 21$ and $2 + 1 = 3$. The number is therefore divisible by 3. On the other hand, the number 562,789,012 has a digit sum of 4 and is therefore not divisible by 3.

This brings up an interesting point. The digit sum of a number is not affected if the order of the digits in it is changed or if zeros are inserted. The digit sum of 124 is 7 and 7 is also the digit sum of 241, of 142, of 412, of 1204, of 4210, and so on. Therefore if 8997 is divisible by 3 because its digit sum is 6, then 9897, 7899, 9978, 708,909, and all other numbers of this family are also divisible by 3.

This can be helpful in some cases. If you know that 15 is divisible by 3, you know that 51 is, too, and so are 105 and 501. You don't even have to add up the digits (though that is easy enough, to be sure, in this case).

It is easy to go from divisibility by 3 to divisibility by 6. If we start with 0 and count by sixes, we have:

0	6	12	18	24
30	36	42	48	54, etc.

If we compare this list with the one made when we counted by threes, we see that we are taking every other number in the former list. We start with 0, skip 3 and take 6, skip 9 and take 12, skip 15 and take 18, and so on. In fact, we are skipping all the odd numbers in the count-by-threes list and taking all the even numbers.

This means that if the digit system of a number is 0, 3, or 6 and if the number is also even it is divisible by 6 (and, of course, by 3, too). If, on the contrary, the digit sum adds up to 0, 3, or 6 and the number is odd, then the number is divisible by 3 but *not* by 6. Thus, 5241, with a digit sum of 3, is odd, so it is divisible by 3 but not by 6. On the other hand, 7302 has a digit sum of 3 and is even, so it is divisible by 6 as well as by 3.

And what about 9? If we start with 0 and count by nines, we have:

0	9	18	27	36
45	54	63	72	81, etc.

This time, if we work out the digit sums (remembering to cast out nines) we find that the digit sum is always 0. Moreover, the digit sum of any number not in the list is always some value other than 0; never 0.

That makes it easy. Any number with a digit sum of 0 is divisible by 9. Any number with a digit sum not equal to 0 is not divisible by 9.

Consider the number 682,900,767. We can cast out 9 and $2 + 7$. This leaves us $6 + 8 + 6 + 7 = 27$ and, casting out $2 + 7$, leaves us 0. Hence the original number is divisible by 9.

As in the case of 3, divisibility by 9 does not depend on the order of digits in the number, since that does not affect the digit sum. If 5427 is divisible by 9 (as it *is*), so are 4572, 7254, 720,504, and so on. If you know for a fact that 18 is divisible by 9, you know that 81, 108, 8010, and 8001 are divisible by 9, without even bothering to add digits.

This sort of thing, does *not* hold for divisibility by 6, because that depends not only on a digit sum but also on the quality of being even. Thus, 36 has a digit sum of 0 and is even; hence it is divisible by 6. Reverse the digits to 63 and the digit sum is still 0, but now the number is not even, so that 63 is *not* divisible by 6.

For divisibility by 2, 4, 5, or 8, where the rule does not depend on digit sums at all, the order of the digits must make a great deal of difference. Thus 16 is divisible by 8, by 4, and by 2, but 61 is divisible by none of those numbers. Again, 15 is divisible by 5, but 51 is not.

OTHER DIVISIBILITIES

Let's summarize. We have rules for telling divisibility by 2, 3, 4, 5, 6, 8, 9, and 10. Dividing by 0 is not allowed and dividing by 1 serves no purpose. That leaves us with one number less than 10 for which I have worked out no rule for divisibility. That number is 7. Unfortunately, there is no good rule for divisibility by 7. The best way to tell whether a number is divisible by 7 is actually to go through the process of dividing.

This is too bad, but since the rules fail us in only one case out of ten, I suppose we shouldn't complain. To make up for it, there is the possibility of telling divisibility quickly for some numbers higher than 10. To see how that works, let's consider first the manner in which numbers can be divided evenly by other numbers. (A number which divides another number evenly is a "factor" of that other number — 2 is a factor of 8 and 3 is a factor of 12.)

In the first place, every number is divisible by 1, giving as a quotient the number itself. In the second place, every number is divisible by itself, giving 1 as a quotient. (In algebraic notation we would say that $n/1 = n$ and $n/n = 1$.) There are no exceptions to this rule; every number has itself and 1 as factors.

We next ask, how many numbers are divisible by numbers other than 1 and themselves? It turns out that this includes most numbers, as a matter of fact, and from now on we will consider only numbers other than 1 and the number itself. Thus, 10 has 2 and 5 for factors; 12 has 2, 3, 4, and 6 for factors; and 60 has 2, 3, 4, 5, 6, 10, 12, 15, 20, and 30 for factors. Numbers possessing such factors are "composite numbers," and 10, 12, and 60 are examples of these.

Yet there are some numbers that are divisible *only* by themselves and 1. Such numbers are called "prime numbers," or simply "primes." Several of the small numbers are primes: 2, 3, 5, and 7. So are 11, 13, 17, 19.

It might seem to you that as numbers get larger and larger, the number of factors they possess increase, because there are more and more smaller numbers to serve as possible factors. This is true for some numbers, such as 10, which has two factors, 12, which has four factors, and 60, with 10 factors.

However, no matter how far you go in the number scale, there will always be numbers with very few factors; and there will be primes, too — numbers with no factors at all but themselves and 1. Immediately after 60, with ten factors, you have 61 with no factors at all (except itself and 1, of course). Again, 5237 is a prime. There are 5235 different numbers smaller than itself (not counting 1), but not one of these will serve as a factor for 5237. Not one of them will divide 5237 evenly. There are numbers far, far larger than 5237 — numbers made up of thousands of digits — that are known to be prime. In principle, numbers of any size can be primes.

It is harder, usually, to check for divisibility by a prime than by a composite number. Fortunately, the three smallest primes, 2, 3, and 5 can be checked easily, but the one number under 10 which gives trouble is 7, and that is a prime. For any prime over 10, it is too much to expect a simple rule. Consequently, we can forget about easy rules for divisibility by 11, 13, 17, or 19.

What about 12, though? That is not a prime, because it can be expressed as the product of factors other than itself and 1. In fact, this can be done in two ways: $12 = 4 \times 3$ and $12 = 6 \times 2$. Any number that is divisible by 12 is divisible first by 4 and then by 3, or first by 6 and then by 2. Thus, $96 \div 12 = 8$, and we also find that $96 \div 4 = 24$ and $24 \div 3 = 8$, or that $96 \div 6 = 16$ and $16 \div 2 = 8$. To check for divisibility by 12, therefore, we might divide by 6 and see if we have an even number as a quotient (for if the quotient is even we know that it can be divided by 2). This will work, but it requires an actual division. Is there no way to work on the original number and check whether that original number is divisible by both 6 and by 2?

Unfortunately that is not useful. If you remember, a number is divisible by 6 when its digit sum is 0, 3, or 6 and when the number itself is even. But if the number is even, then it is already divisible by 2. This means that any number divisible by 6 is automatically divisible by 2, and this automatically spoils things. Half the numbers divisible by 6 are also divisible by 12 (examples are 36, 60, and 84), but the other half are not divisible by 12 (examples 42, 54, and 66). Since all of them are divisible by 2, we cannot distinguish the right ones from the wrong ones. We must divide by 6 first, then check the quotient for divisibility by 2; or we can divide by 2 and then check the quotient for divisibility by 6. In either case, we must actually divide.

Whenever we consider two numbers, one of which is divisible by the other, then any number divisible by the larger number is automatically divisible by the smaller number as well. Accordingly, any number that is divisible by 21 is automatically divisible by 7 or by 3. Any number divisible by 60 is automatically divisible by 2, by 3, by 4, by 5, by 6, by 10, by 12, by 15, by 20, and by 30. And as soon as divisibility is automatic, we can learn nothing new by such a division.

But what if we consider $12 = 4 \times 3$. The number 4 is not divisible by 3 and 3 is not divisible by 4. This means that a number divisible by 4 is *not* automatically divisible by 3, and one divisible by 3 is not automatically divisible by 4. Thus, 28 is divisible by 4 but not by 3; and 27 is divisible by 3 but not by 4. Under these conditions, if a number is divisible by *both* 4 and 3, it must be divisible by 4×3 — that is, by 12.

For instance, the number 312 has a digit sum of 6, so it is divisible by 3. Its last two digits, 12, are divisible by 4, so the whole number is divisible by 4. Since it is divisible by both 3 and 4, it is divisible by 12; and indeed $312 \div 12 = 26$.

In the same way, $15 = 3 \times 5$. Since 5 is not divisible by 3 or 3 by 5, the two numbers can be used together to test divisibility by 15. If a number ends in a 5 or 0 (so that it is divisible by 5) and also has a digit sum of 0, 3, or 6 (so that it is divisible by 3), the number is divisible by 15. You can tell at little more than a glance that 540, 450, and 405 are all divisible by 15, but that 504, 305 and 100 are not.

The number 18 can be represented as 6×3, but that is no help since 6 is divisible by 3 and any number divisible by 6 is automatically divisible by 3 also. However, $18 = 9 \times 2$ and neither of these numbers is divisible by the other. Therefore, if a number is even (so that it is divisible by 2) and has a digit sum of 0 (so that it is divisible by 9), the number is divisible by 18.

As for 14, that can be represented as 7×2, and neither number is divisible by the other. Nevertheless, since there is no simple rule for divisibility by 7, there is none for divisibility by 14 either.

The number 16 can be represented as 4×4 and 8×2. In both cases, divisibility rears its ugly head, because 4 is divisible by 4 and 8 is divisible by 2. This means that some sort of division must be carried through. The best that can be done is to stick to the

last four digits of a number and see if those digits can
be divided by 4 to give a quotient divisible by 4; or to
see if those digits can be divided by 8 to give an even
quotient. I don't think this qualifies as a particularly
quick and easy method.

We end, then, by having reasonably simple rules for
divisibility by 2, 3, 4, 5, 6, 8, 9, 10, 12, 15, and 18.

It is easy sometimes to change a division that is going
to involve a remainder into one that will not. Instead
of carrying through the division to find what the remainder is, you extract the remainder first, then work
out the division to get a quotient without a remainder.
There is no arithmetical reason for this, but there can
be a psychological one. You may feel more comfortable with the division if you know in advance you won't
have to worry about a remainder.

To illustrate: if a number is odd, we subtract 1 to
make it even and it is then divisible by 2. The 1 which
we subtracted will be the remainder. Thus, if you are
faced with $39 \div 2$, reduce the 39 to 38 and $38 \div 2 =$
19. Therefore $39 \div 2 = 19$, with a remainder of 1. In
the same way, you can reduce a number by just enough
to convert the final digit to a 5 or 0 in order to ensure
its divisibility by 5. Thus $48 - 3 = 45$; and $45 \div 5 = 9$;
therefore $48 \div 5 = 9$, with a remainder of 3.

Once you have worked out the digit sum of a number,
it is easy to convert it to a smaller number that is divisible by 9. Consider 5712, which has a digit sum of
6. If you subtract the 6 from 5712, you will have 5706,

which is divisible by 9. The remainder has been safely extracted before the division has even been begun.

In like manner you can subtract enough to make the digit sum either 0, 3, or 6 (whichever is closest) and ensure divisibility by 3. Thus, the number 73,411 has a digit sum of 7. It is enough to subtract 1, to give a digit sum of 6, and 73,410 is divisible by 3.

For divisibility by 6 there is one added complication. Consider the number 12,304, which has a digit sum of 1. If we subtract 1 from the number, making it 12,303, the digit sum becomes 0, which is one of the requirements for divisibility by 6. However, the number is not even, so we must subtract enough to bring it to the next appropriate digit sum. If we subtracted 4 from 12,304 to get 12,300, the digit sum would be 6 and the number would be even. Consequently, 12,300 is divisible by 6.

Divisibility by 4 requires a rather similar device. If a number is odd, subtract 1 and check the last two digits for divisibility by 4. If it is not divisible by 4, subtract 3 rather than 1 to get it to the next lower even number. (You can see for yourself how to handle divisibility by 8)

THE DIVISION TABLE

Telling whether a dividend is divisible by a particular divisor and extracting a remainder to begin with may be amusing but it is only of psychological advantage. Eventually you will have to divide, and even if a remainder does not exist, or if it has been eliminated, division remains the most difficult of the four arithmetical operations.

Division is a backward process, based on our knowledge of multiplication. Everyone memorizes the multiplication table, but no one memorizes a "division table" because that is only the multiplication table worked backward. If you are asked to solve $72 \div 9$, you know the answer is 8, because you have already memorized the fact that $8 \times 9 = 72$. In the same way, you know that $56 \div 7 = 8$, that $48 \div 6 = 8$, that $63 \div 9 = 7$, and the like. You may even know offhand that $72 \div 6 = 12$, that $45 \div 15 = 3$, and so on, simply from remembering that $12 \times 6 = 72$ and $15 \times 3 = 45$. However, all that is really necessary for any division, no matter how complicated, is to know the "division table" (that is, the reverse of the multiplication table) from $81 \div 9 = 9$ to $1 \div 1 = 1$.

This act of knowing the division table teaches us more about division than many of us suspect. Remember that 0 divided by any number — any number at all — gives a quotient of 0. Suppose, then, that we are faced with $90 \div 3$. We know that the 9 divided by 3 is 3 and the 0 divided by 3 (or by any other number) is 0. The quotient of $90 \div 3$ is therefore 30. In fact, we can bring down the zeros without worrying about dividing them at all, so that $900 \div 3 = 300$, $9000 \div 3 = 3000$, and so on. For these divisions we need remember no more than the mere fact that $9 \div 3 = 3$.

In the same way, we know at once that $720 \div 9 = 80$; that $6300 \div 7 = 900$; that $81,000 \div 9 = 9000$, and so on.

Nor are we through. What if we add a zero to the divisor? In other words, what if we consider $90 \div 30$? We know the answer must be 3, because $30 \times 3 = 90$. We can try similar problems and work them out from our knowledge of multiplication so that we see that $900 \div 30 = 30$, $9000 \div 300 = 30$, $90,000 \div 30 = 3000$, and so on.

But we shouldn't have to work out each problem separately. Instead, we can consider that division is the reverse of multiplication. When two numbers, each ending in one or more zeros, are multiplied, the product ends in a number of zeros equal to the sum of those in multiplicand and multiplier. If the multiplication were a division, one would expect that the quotient would end in a number of zeros equal to the *difference* of those in the dividend and divisor.

This is so in the cases I have cited, and we can cite any number of others. If we are faced with $27,000 \div 30$, we have three zeros ending the dividend and one zero ending the divisor. We can expect $3 - 1$, or 2 zeros, ending the quotient. Since $27 \div 3 = 9$, we can confidently say, with no further thought, that $27,000 \div 30 = 900$. In the same way, $2,700,000 \div 900$ will have a quotient ending in $5 - 2$, or 3 zeros, so the answer is 3000.

(You may wonder what happens if the divisor has more zeros than the dividend, as in the example $7770 \div$

700. We'll get to that later in the book.)

There are, of course, innumerable division problems that can't be handled directly out of the division table. I've just mentioned one — 7770 ÷ 700. For the time being let's drop the zeros in the divisor and consider it 7770 ÷ 7. What we can do is divide each digit by 7 and the answer then is 1110. In the same way 369 ÷ 3 = 123, 484 ÷ 4 = 121, and so on.

It may be that a particular digit cannot be divided by a particular divisor, and in that case there is nothing to prevent us from taking the digits two at a time, or even three at a time. We might wish to get the answer to 6,364,812 ÷ 6. Let's consider the dividend in parts as (6)(36)(48)(12). Dividing each part by 6, we have (1)(06)(08)(02) and the answer is 1,060,802.

The only difficulty here is that we must remember to keep the number of digits in the quotient the same as the number in the dividend. If we had divided (36) (48)(12) by 6 to give (6)(8)(2), our answer would have been 682, which would have been wildly wrong.

Placing a 0 before a number (or placing any number of zeros before it) does not change the value of a number. We are perfectly justified in saying that 36 ÷ 6 = 06, if we want to keep the number of digits in the quotient the same as in the dividend, for 06 = 6. For that matter, 006 = 6 and 000,000,000,006 = 6.

The only reason this seems strange to you is that it is customary to drop all those zeros when they are at the very beginning of a whole number. For instance, we say that $36 \div 4 = 9$. Why bother writing 09? However, it is only at the *beginning* of a whole number that we can drop zeros. If we have the number 109, you can bet we can't drop that zero, for 109 does *not* equal 19. Therefore if we are dividing 327 by 3, and consider 327 as $(3)(27) \div 3$, we had better find the quotient to be $(1)(09)$ or 109.

For further examples consider the following. With $6453 \div 3$, write this as $(6)(45)(3) \div 3$ and you see at once that the answer is $(2)(15)(1)$ or 2151. In 910,836 $\div 9$, we have $(9)(108)(36) \div 9 = (1)(012)(04)$ or 101,204.

REWRITING DIVISIONS

Obviously, we cannot always break up a number into convenient groups of digits. Even simple cases may stump us. Take $897 \div 3$. We can divide 9 by 3, but what can we do with the 8 and the 7? Dividing it as $(89)(7)$ doesn't help much; nor does $(8)(97)$. There is the school method, of course, which is slow, steady, and sure — and involves carrying. We say, "First, 8 divided by 3 equals 2 with 2 left over. Put down 2 and make the 9 a 29. Now 29 divided by 3 equals 9 with 2 left over. Put down 9 and make the 7 a 27. Finally, 27 divided by 3 equals 9 with nothing left over. Put down 9, and the answer is 299."

Here's the way it looks in figures:

$$3)\ \underline{8_2 9_2 7}$$
$$2\ 9\ 9$$

(This is an example of "short division.")

The difficulty in the school method lies chiefly — as always — in the carrying. Is there any way whereby the dividend can be converted into a number, or group of numbers, in which there is no carrying because all the digits, or small groups of digits, are divisible by the divisor?

Well, suppose that we wrote 897 as 900 − 3. Both 900 and 3 are easily divided by 3; at a glance, in fact. The only question is: How does one go about dividing 900 − 3 by 3? In algebraic notation it is easy to show that $\frac{a-b}{c} = \frac{a}{c} - \frac{b}{c}$. To divide 900 − 3 by 3, it is only necessary to divide 900 by 3, then 3 by 3 and subtract the second quotient from the first. In other words $(900 - 3) \div 3 = (900 \div 3) - (3 \div 3)$. Instead of worrying about $897 \div 3$, we say $(900 - 3) \div 3 = 300 - 1 = 299$. The answer is ours in a moment.

Likewise, in dividing 756 by 4, we can write 756 as 800 − 44. Well, $(800 - 44) \div 4 = 200 - 11 = 189$. Or, if faced with $2376 \div 8$, we can write 2376 as 2400 − 24. Now we have $(2400 - 24) \div 8 = 300 - 3 = 297$.

We are not restricted to subtraction, either. If we want $135 \div 3$, we can write 135 as 120 + 15. With the problem $(120 + 15) \div 3$, the answer is 40 + 5 or 45. Or, if we want to divide 285 by 5, we try it $(250 + 35) \div 5 = 50 + 7 = 57$. We might just as well have written 285 as 300 − 15. Then, $(300 - 15) \div 5 = 60 -$

$3 = 57$. The exact route by which you arrive at a quick and easy answer is up to you, and, once you understand the principles involved, you can pick your route at will.

The system will work for larger numbers too, of course. To divide 176,968 by 8, we might decide to write 176,968 as $160,000 + 16,000 + 800 + 168$. Dividing that sum by 8 we get $20,000 + 2000 + 100 + 21$, for an answer of 22,121. Here, however, the number of figures involved becomes so large that you lose enough time working it out, perhaps, to make you decide to go back to carrying.

But wait, we need not stop at writing the dividend as a sum or difference. Might there not be something we could do to the divisor to simplify matters?

If dividing by 8, for instance, let's remember that $8 = 2 \times 2 \times 2$ and that, therefore, instead of saying $176,968 \div 8$, we could say $176,968 \div 2 \div 2 \div 2$. The advantage of substituting three divisions for one is that each of the three divisions is by 2 and dividing by 2 is simpler than dividing by any other number. Well, then, let's carry through the division of 176,968 in the following manner:

$$
\begin{array}{r}
2)\ \underline{176,968} \\
2)\ \underline{88,484} \\
2)\ \underline{44,242} \\
22,121
\end{array}
$$

There is your answer. Even the necessity of carrying isn't much of a chore in the case of division by 2, and the chances are that you will arrive at the answer more quickly and painlessly through dividing by 2 three times than through dividing by 8 once.

For smaller numbers the same process can be used mentally, if you choose. If we were to try to work out $192 \div 8$ directly, it might take a few moments of time. If we were to divide 192 by 2 three times and say to ourselves 96, 48, 24, we would have the answer 24 almost at once.

So far, in discussing actual divisions, the examples I have used have happened to come out evenly. But suppose they don't. In the first place, you can sometimes arrange to have them come out evenly without any trouble. If asked to divide 347 by 3, you can see that 347 has the digit sum 5 and is therefore not divisible by 3. If you reduce 347 by 2 to 345, you will have a digit sum of 3, and 345 is therefore divisible by 3. If you look upon 345 as $(3)(45)$ you can see instantly that $345 \div 3 = 115$. Remembering the 2 which you had previously removed, you know the answer to $347 \div 3$ is $115\frac{2}{3}$.

If the dividend is large, it may take a while to check its divisibility and correct it, especially if the divisor is, let us say, 8. Suppose that we wanted to solve $176,975 \div 8$. We could tell that the division will not come out even because the last three digits, 975, are not divisible by 8. It would take some time, however, to work out the fact that we ought to reduce the number by 7 to achieve divisibility by 8. In that time we might well have gone through the complete division by the ordinary method and obtained the answer.

But suppose that we divide 176, 975 by 8 exactly as it is, without worrying about remainders, and see what happens:

$$
\begin{array}{ll}
2) \ \overline{176,975} & \\
2) \ \overline{\ \ 88,487} & \text{and 1 left over} \\
2) \ \overline{\ \ 44,243} & \text{and 1 left over} \\
\quad \ \ 22,121 & \text{and 1 left over}
\end{array}
$$

What if you simply ignore the remainders and state the answer to be 22,121? How wrong are you? Not very; the correct answer is 22,121⅞. You are wrong by less than 1. Whenever you break up a divisor and substitute many divisions by small numbers for one division by a large number, then — no matter how many remainders you forget about and no matter how large the remainders are — the end result is that your answer is wrong by less than 1.

If the quotient is large, a mistake by less than 1 may not be important. Certainly, if absolute accuracy is not required, the loss of a fraction is worth a saving in time.

LONG DIVISION

So far, of course, I have been dealing with divisors containing but a single digit, and that means I have been restricting myself to only the simplest part of the subject. When dealing with one-digit divisors, we can even make out, if we must, with the usual method of short division. For instance, if we divided 8,563,990,806 by 7, we could do it this way:

$$7\overline{)\ 8,_15_16_23,_29_19_50,_18_40_56}$$
$$1,\ 2\ 2\ 3,\ 4\ 2\ 7,\ 2\ 5\ 8$$

Carrying is involved, of course, and we can write down the numbers carried, making them small to avoid confusion with the digits of the dividend.

With practice it becomes quite possible to keep the numbers being carried in the head and simply write the example this way:

$$7\overline{)\ 8,563,990,806}$$
$$1,223,427,258$$

This isn't really too bad. There may be no good method for simplifying division by 7, but we can grit our teeth and bear it.

However, in dividing by one-digit divisors we are always working within the limits of the division table, where we know all the answers by heart. We know that 7 goes into 8 one time with 1 left over. We know that 7 goes into 18 two times with 4 left over. What if we divide our large dividend by 18, though? Now we move outside the division table. Consider 8,563,990,806 ÷ 18. We know that 18 won't go into 8 even once, so we move on and consider how many times 18 will go into 85 and what, if anything, is the remainder. That's not so easy.

Let's see, now. If we multiply 18 by 2 the answer is 36, and twice that is 72, so $18 \times 4 = 72$. If we add another 18 we get 90, so $18 \times 5 = 90$, and since that is over 85 and too high we'll stop at 4 and place that in the quotient. Furthermore, $85 - 72 = 13$, so that is the remainder. That makes the next digit 136 and the next problem $136 \div 18$.

Unless we are mental marvels, this sort of thing is simply more than we can do in our heads, so we work it out, in full, on paper. It would look like this:

```
                    475,777,267
          18 ) 8,563,990,806
                7 2
                ───
                1 36
                1 26
                ────
                  103
                   90
                  ────
                  13 9
                  12 6
                  ────
                   1 39
                   1 26
                   ────
                    130
                    126
                    ───
                     4 8
                     3 6
                     ───
                     1 20
                     1 08
                     ────
                      126
                      126
                      ───
                        0
```

This is "long division," and of all the processes of grade school arithmetic it is undoubtedly the most hated. Most adults never recover from that hatred. *I* hate it.

Well, then, let's remember the first basic rule: change something difficult into something easy. If we find long division hateful and short division bearable, we should search for methods of converting long division into short division. Since long division is brought on by divisors of more than one digit and short division involves divisors of just one digit, let's concentrate on the divisor. We know that $18 = 9 \times 2$; therefore a number $\div 18$ gives the same answer it would give if it were $\div 9 \div 2$, or $\div 2 \div 9$.

Does it matter whether we divide first by 9 and then by 2, or first by 2 and then by 9? As far as getting the correct answer is concerned, no; we end with the same answer in both cases. However, the smaller the divisor the easier the division, so why not divide by the smaller number first? Then when we have to turn to division by a larger number we have a smaller dividend to work with.

If we work first with 2 and then with 9 our problem becomes:

$$2 \overline{)\ 8{,}563{,}990{,}806}$$
$$9 \overline{)\ 4{,}281{,}995{,}403}$$
$$475{,}777{,}267$$

The long division has been replaced by two short divisions. The two short divisions have not perhaps been the easiest thing in the world and have required a little concentration, but they probably have taken you a lot less time and tension than the single long division would have done.

In the example just given, dividing by 9 was more difficult than dividing by 2 and undoubtedly caused most of what delay was involved in getting the solution. But then, $9 = 3 \times 3$, so instead of $\div$ 9 you might work with $\div$ 3 $\div$ 3. Now the problem becomes:

$$
\begin{array}{r}
2 \overline{)\ 8{,}563{,}990{,}806} \\
3 \overline{)\ 4{,}281{,}995{,}403} \\
3 \overline{)\ 1{,}427{,}331{,}801} \\
475{,}777{,}267
\end{array}
$$

It's up to you. If you find that dividing once by 9 isn't very difficult, and that it takes less time than dividing twice by 3, stick to 9.

I only used a large dividend to demonstrate the principle. You are much more likely to run into smaller numbers in the ordinary course of life. An example would be the problem $252 \div 18$. Despite the smallness of the dividend, this could plunge you into long division, too. But suppose that instead you divide 252 first by 2, then by 3, then by 3. You would find that $252 \div 2 = 126$, $126 \div 3 = 42$, and $42 \div 3 = 14$. Each of these three divisions, far from requiring long division, can be done with perfect ease at a stroke, and in the head. The result is that you see that $252 \div 18 = 14$ without trouble or pain, and certainly without long division.

If you are dividing by 12, you can divide first by 3, then by 4, since $3 \times 4 = 12$; or you can divide by 2, then by 2, then by 3, since $2 \times 2 \times 3 = 12$. How about $432 \div 12$? Well, $432 \div 2 = 216$; $216 \div 2 = 108$; $108 \div 3 = 36$, and that is the answer.

Naturally, one can go too far and make too many divisions. Since $2 \times 2 \times 3 \times 3 = 36$, you can change a division by 36 into two successive divisions by 2 followed by two successive divisions by 3. You may find that four divisions are confusing and that you can get along perfectly well with only three $(3 \times 3 \times 4 = 36)$, or even two $(4 \times 9 = 36)$. If you have an aversion to division by 9 but would still like to have only two divisions, you might try $6 \times 6 = 36$.

It makes no difference which route you take. Consider:

$432 \div 36 = 12$
$432 \div 2 = 216$; $216 \div 2 = 108$;
$\qquad\qquad\qquad\qquad 108 \div 3 = 36$; $36 \div 3 = 12$
$432 \div 3 = 144$; $144 \div 3 = 48$; $48 \div 4 = 12$
$432 \div 4 = 108$; $108 \div 9 = 12$
$432 \div 6 = 72$; $72 \div 6 = 12$

The answer is the same in every case, so you may as well choose that route which is quickest and easiest for you. For myself, I find the division first by 4 and then by 9 the easiest, because $432 \div 4$ immediately can be seen to be 108 if I consider 432 as $(4)(32)$, and because I happen to know offhand that $108 \div 9 = 12$. For you a different route may be easier. Suit yourself by all means, so long as the answer remains correct.

(You may ask how one can know which is the easiest method for oneself. The answer is time. If you practise quick and easy math long enough, you'll begin to get the feel for what you can do best. It will begin to "come natural.")

Of course, not all potential long divisions are so easily handled. Remember that there are prime numbers. What do we do if we must divide by 13 instead of by 12, or by 19 instead of by 18, or by 37 instead of by 36? The numbers 13, 19, and 37 are primes, and if you are stuck with division by them (or by any other prime) you cannot break up the division into one-digit steps.

Even if a number can be broken up into factors, some of the factors may be primes that are too large to handle. You might have to divide by 133. This divisor can be expressed as 7×19, but 19 is a prime and can be broken down no further. In such cases, especially if you feel you must have an exact answer, there may be nothing to do but face the music and get busy with your long division. That at least will work no matter what the divisor is. Remember once again what I said at the beginning of the book. The school methods sometimes may be slow, but they are *sure*.

If, on the contrary, you would be content with answers that are *nearly* right, provided you can get them quickly, there remains a chance. I will have a few more words to say on this subject later in the book.

CHECKING DIVISION

In division as in subtraction we have the problem that the order in which dividend and divisor are written cannot be changed: $a \div b$ is *not* equal to $b \div a$. However, in subtraction we could reverse matters by switching to addition; and in division we can reverse matters by switching to multiplication. If $a \div b = c$, then $c \times b = a$. This means that in any division the quotient times the divisor must equal the dividend.

Accordingly, if you have worked out $2812 \div 37 = 76$ and wish to check your answer, it is inefficient to go over your figures and do nothing more: you may make the same mistake over again. Instead, reverse matters and consider 76×37. The product should be 2812. If it is not, then you have made a mistake either in the original division or in the check multiplication and you had better search carefully. If the product comes out to 2812, then you are almost certainly correct (unless you have made mistakes in both the division and multiplication that balance each other — which is extremely unlikely) and you may relax.

Naturally, this works in quick and easy techniques as well as in examples worked out in full. If you have solved $984 \div 8$ by dividing 984 three times by 2 to get $492, 246, 123$ — with 123 your answer — you can check by doubling 123 three times. You find that beginning with 123 you have $246, 492, 984$. The check product equals the original dividend and you are all right.

But what if the quotient is not a whole number?

What if there is a remainder? The remainder represents the quantity which, when subtracted from the dividend, makes the dividend divisible. Suppose, for instance, you found that $895 \div 17 = 52$ with a remainder of 11. (The answer would then usually be written $52\frac{11}{17}$.) If the 11 were subtracted from 895 you would get 884 and that would be divisible by 17. It would turn out that $884 \div 17 = 52$. Once you have subtracted the remainder from the dividend and achieved divisibility you can carry through the usual check. Since $52 \times 17 = 884$, your division was correct. (Of course, you might make an error in subtracting the remainder from the dividend, but be careful and you won't.)

Division can be checked by casting out nines, too. Suppose we have worked out $99,934 \div 58 = 1723$. In the dividend we cast out the three 9's, and the digit sum is 7. In the divisor, $5 + 8 = 13$ and $1 + 3 = 4$, which is the digit sum there. In the quotient we cast out the $7 + 2$ and the digit sum is $1 + 3 = 4$. The digit-sum division becomes $7 \div 4 = 4$. This does not look right at first glance, but remember that we can add 9 (or any number of 9's) to any of the digit sums without changing the essential nature of the situation. If we add 9 to the 7, the division becomes $16 \div 4 = 4$, which is correct and which shows the division is probably without an error.

You may not want to go to the trouble of trying to figure out where to add a 9 and how many to add. We can therefore reverse the situation in the usual manner and make a digit-sum multiplication out of the digit-sum division. If $7 \div 4 = 4$, then $4 \times 4 = 7$. By ordinary arithmetic, $4 \times 4 = 16$ and $1 + 6 = 7$ all right, so the digit sums check.

And yet here again we must ask: What if the division doesn't come out even? Consider the case of $5556 \div 17 = 326\frac{14}{17}$. There is here a remainder of 14. Again, we subtract 14 from the dividend to make it divisible. The dividend shrinks from 5556 to 5542 and the smaller number is divisible, for $5542 \div 17 = 326$.

You can check this second division by casting out nines. For $5542 \div 17 = 326$, the digit sums come out to $7 \div 8 = 2$. Add 9 to the 7 and get $16 \div 8 = 2$, which is correct. Or reverse matters and say that $2 \times 8 = 7$. Since $2 \times 8 = 16$ and $1 + 6 = 7$, that is correct. The division is checked.

You can, if you wish, subtract the remainder from the dividend at the digit-sum stage. Consider again $5556 \div 17 = 326\frac{14}{17}$, and take digit sums as they are. The digit sum of 5556 is 3, that of 17 is 8, that of 326 is 2, and that of 14 (the remainder) is 5. The digit-sum division becomes $3 \div 8 = 2$, with a remainder of 5. Now subtract the remainder digit sum from the dividend digit sum, $3 - 5$. To make this possible increase the 3 by 9 to 12. We have $12 - 5 = 7$, which is the new digit sum of the dividend. With the remainder now removed, we have $7 \div 8 = 2$, which, as we showed in the previous paragraph, is correct.

6

Decimals

THANKS to the way in which our number system is built up, it is particularly easy to multiply or divide by 10. Let's start with the number 243, for example (any other number would do), and multiply it by 10. The answer is 2430. Multiply that product by 10 again, and we have 24,300; by 10 again, and it is 243,000; again and it is 2,430,000. Each multiplication by 10 adds another zero to the number but doesn't change any of the digits.

Now, let's begin with 2,430,000 and try dividing by 10; the answer is 243,000. Divide that by 10 and the new quotient is 24,300; divide by 10 again and you have 2430; still again and you have 243. Each division by 10 removes one of the zeros.

In order to see what this means let us supply the number 243 with a series of zeros to use for the purpose of multiplying by 10, placing them on the paper to begin with instead of having them appear out of nowhere. In order to make sure we don't confuse this supply of zeros with zeros that may actually form part of the number itself, let's put a period after the digits making up the actual number. (After all, it is customary to use a period to indicate "stop.") The zeros to the right of the period would then represent the reserve supply.

We can write 243 this way, in other words:

243.0000000000000000000000000

Or, if we choose, with as many additional zeros for which we have room, and the patience, to write.

If we multiply 243 with its reserve supply of zeros by 10, then by 10 again, then by 10 again, and so on, we get the following numbers (the period always marking the end of the actual number).

> 2,430.000000000000000000000
> 24,300.00000000000000000000
> 243,000.0000000000000000000
> 2,430,000.000000000000000
> 24,300,000.00000000000000
> 243,000,000.0000000000000, etc.

If we take the final number above and start dividing by 10, we get the following succession of numbers:

> 24,300,000.00000000000000
> 2,430,000.000000000000000
> 243,000.00000000000000000
> 24,300.0000000000000000000
> 2,430.000000000000000000000
> 243.00000000000000000000000

The period I have been using is called a "decimal point," from a Latin word for "ten" because it came to be used in connection with multiplying and dividing by

10. If we look upon the multiplication by 10 and the division by 10 in the manner I have just presented, we see that we are not so much adding and subtracting zeros as merely moving the decimal point.

Every time you multiply a number by 10, the decimal point moves one place to the right. If you divide by 10, it moves one place to the left. If you try to multiply by 100, you will find that the decimal point moves two places to the right, while multiplying by 1000 will move it three places to the right. Dividing by 100 will move the decimal point two places to the left, and dividing it by 1000 will move it three places to the left.

The number of places it moves is equal to the number of zeros in the multiplier or diviser; multiplication always involving a rightward movement and division a leftward movement.

If you practise this sort of thing, you will see that this explains why the number of zeros at the end of a product is equal to the sum of the zeros at the end of the multiplicand and the multiplier. It also explains why the number of zeros at the end of a quotient is equal to the zeros at the end of the dividend minus the zeros at the end of the divisor.

But now a question arises. Imagine taking the number 243 and dividing it by 10. If we write the number with the reserve supply of zeros as 243.000000 (or as many zeros as we want), we might suppose that we ought to move the decimal point leftward again, even though there are no more zeros to the left of the decimal point. The number would then become 24.30000000, and we must ask ourselves what such a number can mean — in particular, what a non-zero digit to the right of the decimal point means.

To look into that question, let's reduce our non-zero digits to a bare minimum, a single 1, and deal with the number 100. If we divide that by 10, we have 10 as the quotient. Divide the quotient by 10 again and we have 1. Divide that by 10 still again and we have a fraction $\frac{1}{10}$. Divide that by 10 yet again and we have a fraction $\frac{1}{100}$.

Now let's use the decimal point and write the number 100 with a reserve of zeros (just three or four, for we don't need many) and let's put another reserve of zeros in front. We don't need a decimal point to mark off the reserve in front, since zeros in front of a number don't change its value. There is a difference between 1 and 10, so we need a decimal point in order to write 1.0 and make sure the number stays "one." There is no difference in value, however, between 01 and 1, or even between 00000001 and 1. Consequently, we can write 100 like this:

0000100.00000

If we divide this number by 10, the decimal point moves to the left and we have

000010.00000 — which is 10.

Divide by 10 again and we have

00001.000000 — which is 1.

Now if we again divide by 10 and once more move

the decimal point to the left, we have

0000.1000000

Since we know that 1 divided by 10 is $\frac{1}{10}$, let's say that 0000.1000000 is a way of writing $\frac{1}{10}$.

If we divide once more by 10 and move the decimal point leftward again, we get

000.01000000

We must say this is a way of writing $\frac{1}{100}$.

But now we can make matters clearer by getting rid of the reserve supply of zeros, or at least of as much of the reserve supply as does not serve any useful purpose. We know the reserve supply is there, but we don't have to stare at it continuously.

On the right-hand side of the decimal point let's drop the zeros at the extreme right; on the left-hand side let's drop the zeros at the extreme left. Thus, if we had the number 0000024.300000, we can write it simply as 24.3, remembering that the reserve supply is still there (if invisible) and can be put back as needed at any time. The zeros are "on call."

Of course, one must never drop zeros that are actually part of the number itself and not of the reserve supply. The best way to recognize such essential zeros is to notice that they are bounded either by two non-zero digits or by a decimal point and a non-zero digit. The number 00002004.0030000, for instance, can be written 2004.003. Of the four zeros we have kept the two at the left are bounded by a 2 and a 4 and the two at the right are bounded by the decimal point and a 3.

This means that the number 0000100.0000 can be written 100. The only two zeros that need be kept are those bounded by the 1 and the decimal point; and, indeed, 100 is the usual way of writing "one hundred" and the way in which we are accustomed to see it. We want to include the decimal point, because it is extremely handy in calculation; I have done this by writing the number not as 100 but as 100. with a decimal point.

Just to make sure we notice that the decimal point is there and that we don't think it is a period at the end of a sentence or merely an accidental speck, let's write down just one zero from our invisible reserve supply and write it 100.0. This makes the decimal point quite visible and doesn't alter the value of the number. (Actually, in making measurements 100.0 has a different meaning from 100. Both have the same value of "one hundred," but 100.0 represents a *more accurate* measurement than 100 does. In the arithmetical calculations with which this book is concerned, however, we can ignore this difference and consider 100.0 = 100.)

As we multiply or divide a number written with a decimal point, let's add zeros from our invisible reserve as we need them, or drop zeros back into our invisible reserve when we no longer need them. For example, if we divided 100.0 by 10, we move the decimal point one place to the left and have 10.00 as the quotient. We don't need that last zero, so we'll write it as 10.0 and say that 100.0 ÷ 10 = 10.0, which, of course, is "ten."

Then $10.0 \div 10 = 1.0$, which is "one." If we wish to continue on the basis of a leftward-moving decimal point, we say that $1.0 \div 10 = .1$. Now, in order not to miss the decimal point, let's include one zero from the invisible reserve supply on the left and say $1.0 \div 10 = 0.1$, and consider that 0.1 is the decimal-point way of writing $\frac{1}{10}$. Another division by 10 and we have $0.1 \div 10 = 0.01$, which is the decimal-point way of writing $\frac{1}{100}$.

Digits to the right of the decimal point seem to represent fractions, and such numbers are therefore called "decimal fractions" — or, simply, "decimals."

FREEING THE DECIMAL POINT

Now we are ready to go back to the problem of dividing 243 by 10.

If we worked this out by ordinary arithmetic we would find that $243 \div 10 = 24\frac{3}{10}$. We must not forget that writing a number such as $24\frac{3}{10}$ is just a short way of writing what is actually a sum $24 + \frac{3}{10}$. If we want to express the numbers as decimals, we can write 24 as 24.0 without trouble. As for $\frac{3}{10}$, it isn't difficult to guess that if $\frac{1}{10}$ is 0.1 then $\frac{3}{10}$ ought to be 0.3. So $24\frac{3}{10}$ becomes $24.0 + 0.3$.

Suppose instead that we had divided 243 by 100. The answer by ordinary arithmetic is $243 \div 100 = 2\frac{43}{100}$, or $2 + \frac{43}{100}$. If we remember anything at all about the addition of fractions, we know that $\frac{43}{100}$ can be written as $\frac{40}{100} + \frac{3}{100}$. If we remember how to reduce fractions, we also know that $^{40}\!/_{100}$ can be written as $^4\!/_{10}$. Therefore $2^{43}\!/_{100}$ becomes $2 + ^4\!/_{10} + ^3\!/_{100}$.

We will introduce the decimal point and write 2 as 2.0; and $^4\!/_{10}$ as 0.4. Since $^1\!/_{100}$ is 0.01, $^3\!/_{100}$ ought to be 0.03. We conclude that $2^{43}\!/_{100} = 2.0 + 0.4 + 0.03$.

But now we are faced with sums involving decimals, and how is that worked out?

In adding ordinary numbers, we are taught at the very beginning to place units under units and tens under tens, so that if we add 74 and 5, we write it

$$\text{thus} \quad \begin{array}{r} 74 \\ 5 \\ \hline \end{array} \quad \text{and not thus} \quad \begin{array}{r} 74 \\ 5 \\ \hline \end{array}$$

This should continue beyond the decimal point also. The first place to the right of the decimal point is the "tenth column," the second place to the right is the "hundredth column"; then comes the "thousandth column," and so on. These too should be lined up accurately.

The best way to make sure of this is to see to it that the decimal points all fall in a vertical line. When that is taken care of, all the columns will line up properly on both sides of the decimal point. In other words, to add 24.0 and 0.3, we write it as follows:

$$\begin{array}{r} 24.0 \\ + \ 0.3 \\ \hline 24.3 \end{array}$$

The sum is quite obviously 24.3.

Similarly, if you work out the sum of 2.0, 0.4, and

0.03, keeping the decimal points in a vertical line you will have

$$
\begin{array}{r}
2.0 \\
0.4 \\
0.03 \\
\hline
2.43
\end{array}
$$

Notice that you have the 3 in a column that includes nothing else. That should not be disturbing. We are used to such additions as this:

$$
\begin{array}{r}
305 \\
22 \\
17 \\
\hline
344
\end{array}
$$

We automatically bring down the 3. Of course, you may be thinking about it now for the first time and wondering why that is allowed. Well, try looking at it this way. Suppose that we make use of our reserve of zeros on the left and turn the addition immediately above to

$$
\begin{array}{r}
305 \\
022 \\
017 \\
\hline
344
\end{array}
$$

This is certainly permissible, for 022 and 017 are the same in value as 22 and 17.

Similarly, in the addition of 2.0, 0.4, and 0.03, we could make use of the reserve of zeros on the right and make it

$$2.00$$
$$0.40$$
$$0.03$$
$$\overline{2.43}$$

We are completely justified, then, in reaching the final conclusion that $243.0 \div 10 = 24.3$ and $243.0 \div 100 = 2.43$.

In short, our rule that the decimal point moves one place to the right as you multiply by 10 and one place to the left as you divide by 10 is true even when digits other than zero border the decimal point. The decimal point is completely freed and we can move it through a number at will.

Thus $24.327 \times 100 = 2432.7$ and $24.327 \div 100 = 0.24327$. (For some reason it is not customary to mark off numbers to the right of the decimal point by commas in groups of three, as is done for the numbers to the left of the decimal point.)

Now we have the answer to the question raised earlier in the book as to what happens if the divisor has more zeros than the dividend. To refresh your memory: I said that the zeros ending the quotient were equal in number to those ending the dividend minus those ending the divisor. Thus, $10,000 \div 100 = 100$ (four zeros minus two zeros equal two zeros).

But what happens if we wish to tackle $100 \div 10,000$? Here we have two zeros ending the dividend and four ending the divisor, so that the number of zeros ending the quotient ought to be $2 - 4$, and unless we go into negative numbers that stumps us.

If we forget the old rule and use the decimal point instead, we have $100.0 \div 10,000$. There are four zeros ending 10,000, so we move the decimal point four places to the left (we are dealing with a division) and the example becomes $100.0 \div 10,000 = 0.01$, or $\frac{1}{100}$.

MANIPULATING DECIMALS

You may wonder what other devices used earlier in this book can be replaced by devices involving the decimal point. Fortunately, very few need to be. In fact, one of the important conveniences of decimals is that although they represent fractions they can be treated by the same techniques used for whole numbers.

In addition and subtraction, for instance, it is only necessary to make sure the decimal points line up, and, after that, all the usual rules apply. If we wish to add

$$
\begin{array}{r}
37.3 \\
+19.9 \\
\hline
\end{array}
$$

we subtract 0.1 from the augend and add 0.1 to the addend and have

$$
\begin{array}{r}
37.2 \\
+20.0 \\
\hline
57.2 \\
\end{array}
$$

which gives us our answer at a glance.

Again, instead of writing

$$
\begin{array}{r}
57.5 \\
-22.8 \\
\hline
\end{array}
$$

we add 0.2 to both minuend and subtrahend and have

$$57.7$$
$$-23.0$$
$$\overline{34.7}$$

so that the answer comes quickly.

To understand how multiplication affects numbers with decimal points, let's first try some simple examples involving fractions. You will accept the fact, I think, that $\frac{1}{10} \times 7 = \frac{7}{10}$. If this is converted into decimal form, what we are saying is that $0.1 \times 7 = 0.7$.

You can try other examples of this, and you will see that when a multiplicand containing a decimal point is multiplied by a whole number, the position of the decimal point is not changed. Thus, $2\frac{4}{10} \times 4$ is $(2 + \frac{4}{10}) \times 4$, which equals $8 + \frac{16}{10}$. You know that $\frac{16}{10} = 1\frac{6}{10} = 1 + \frac{6}{10}$. Therefore, $8 + \frac{16}{10} = 8 + 1 + \frac{6}{10}$, or $9\frac{6}{10}$. To summarize: $2\frac{4}{10} \times 4 = 9\frac{6}{10}$. If we place that in decimal form, we are saying that $2.4 \times 4 = 9.6$. If we were to work out other examples in fractional form we would find that $2.4 \times 8 = 19.2$, $0.24 \times 4 = 0.96$, $0.24 \times 8 = 1.92$, and the like.

The digits are as they would be if no decimal point were involved, and the placing of the decimal point is the same in the product as in the multiplicand (provided the multiplier is a whole number). If the decimal point is one place from the right in the multiplicand, it is one place from the right in the product; if it is two places from the right in one, it is two places from the right in the other.

This means that you can follow the ordinary rules of whole-number calculation and then just remember to place the decimal point correctly. If you are multiplying 6.3 by 11, you can forget the decimal point to start with. Since 63×11 is $63 \times (10 + 1)$, the answer is $630 + 63 = 693$, if we consider digits alone. Then, since the decimal point is one place from the right in the multiplicand, 6.3, it is placed similarly in the product, which becomes 69.3.

Or try 2.35×99. Consider it to be 235×99 or $235(100 - 1)$. The answer, as far as digits are concerned, is $23,500 - 235$ or $23,265$. Now place the decimal point two places from the right, as in the multiplicand, and the answer to the problem is 232.65.

Sometimes one or more zeros appear on the extreme right to the right of the decimal point. Let's say that you are faced with 1.422×20. If this were 1422×20, you would represent 20 as 10×2. Multiplying 1422 by 2 gives you 2844 and a multiplication by 10 simply adds a zero at the end to make it 28,440. You want the decimal point three places from the right, however, so it becomes 28.440. If you wish, you can then drop that final zero, and state the answer as 28.44. However, don't drop the zero until after you have placed the decimal point correctly. It is only after the decimal point is in place that the value of the number is fixed, and it is only then that you are safe in dropping (or, to indicate accuracy, not dropping) zeros.

You can even learn to manipulate your decimals without dropping the decimal point. For instance, let's try 1.422 × 20 once more. Again, we break up 20 into 10 × 2, but this time we multiply first by 10 and do that by simply moving the decimal point one place to the right, so that 1.422 becomes 14.22. Now we multiply that by 2 without budging the decimal point, and it becomes 28.44.

But what if the multiplicand and the multiplier are both decimals? What, in other words if we are not multiplying 6.3 by 11, but 6.3 by 1.1.

At this point, let's back up a little and look at some simple multiplications. Consider this: 60 × 4 = 240. Suppose that we divide 60 by 2, getting 30, and multiply 4 by 2 to get 8. If we multiply the new numbers, we find that 30 × 8 gives us the same product as before, 240. If we divide 60 by 5 and multiply 4 by 5, we have 12 × 20, which is still 240. Or what if we multiply 60 by 2 and divide 4 by 2? We have 120 × 2; yes, 240.

If you check further you can satisfy yourself that when two numbers are involved in a multiplication, then multiplying one and dividing the other by the same number leaves the product unchanged. In algebraic notation: $a \times b = ab$. If a is multiplied by n and b is divided by n and the two new numbers are multiplied, you have $an \times b/n = abn/n = ab$. The product is not changed. (You may remember we had a similar situation in addition, where a sum was not changed if the same number was added to the augend and subtracted from the addend.)

Now let's go back to the problem 6.3×1.1. What is troubling us here is the fact that both numbers are decimals. If only one were a decimal we could make the other the multiplier and have the situation where a decimal is multiplied by a whole number, and that we can handle. Let's follow the basic rule, then, of converting a difficult problem into a simple one, and change one of the decimals into a whole number.

We multiply 1.1 by 10; the decimal point moves one place to the right and 1.1 becomes 11. In order to keep our product unchanged, however, we must now divide 6.3 by 10. The decimal point moves one place to the left and 6.3 becomes 0.63. Our multiplication problem is changed from 6.3×1.1 to 0.63×11. Matters are now simple. Since $63 \times 11 = 630 + 63 = 693$, we need only place the decimal point two from the right (as it is in the multiplicand, 0.63), so the answer is 6.93.

Suppose that we have the problem 521.2×0.008. If we multiply 0.008 by 1000, the decimal point moves three places to the right and 0.008 becomes 8. Now we must divide 521.2 by 1000, so the decimal point moves three places to the left and 521.2 becomes 0.5212. The problem has now become 0.5212×8. We double 5212 three times: 10,424, 20,848, and 41,696. In the multiplicand, 0.5212, the decimal point is four places from the right, and it must be so in the product as well. The answer therefore is 4.1696.

Now let us write out the original numbers being multiplied in the two cases just given, without any shift in the decimal points, and place the correct product (as we have determined it) under each:

$$
\begin{array}{r}
6.3 \\
\times\ 1.1 \\
\hline
6.93
\end{array}
\qquad
\begin{array}{r}
521.2 \\
\times\ 0.008 \\
\hline
4.1696
\end{array}
$$

In the first case the decimal point is 1 from the right in the multiplicand, 1 from the right in the multiplier, and 2 from the right in the product. In the second case, the decimal point is 1 from the right in the multiplicand, 3 from the right in the multiplier, and 4 from the right in the product.

You can try this for any number of cases by the methods I have used here and you will find an easy rule for the location of the decimal point in multiplications. The number of places from the right in the product is equal to the sum of the number of places from the right in multiplicand and multiplier.

Assume that we know that $54 \times 12 = 648$. (After all $54 \times 12 = 54 \times (10 + 2) = 540 + 108 = 648$.) In that case, without doing any shifting of decimal points at all, we can say that

$$
\begin{array}{r}
5.4 \\
\times\ 12 \\
\hline
64.8
\end{array}
\qquad
\begin{array}{r}
5.4 \\
\times\ 1.2 \\
\hline
6.48
\end{array}
\qquad
\begin{array}{r}
5.4 \\
\times\ 0.12 \\
\hline
0.648
\end{array}
\qquad
\begin{array}{r}
0.54 \\
\times\ 0.12 \\
\hline
0.0648
\end{array}
\qquad
\begin{array}{r}
0.0054 \\
\times\ 1.2 \\
\hline
0.00648
\end{array}
$$

So the rules for multiplication do not alter for decimals. One need only be careful about placing the decimal point. (This is a matter I will return to later.)

The matter of decimals and division remains. We know that the multiplication of a decimal by a whole number leaves the position of the decimal point unchanged. It is not surprising that the same is true of division. We can check this with fractions: $\frac{9}{10} \div 3 = \frac{3}{10}$. If we write this in decimals, we have $0.9 \div 3 = 0.3$. Similarly, since $75 \div 15 = 5$, then $7.5 \div 15 = 0.5$ and $0.75 \div 15 = 0.05$. You can work this out in fractional form if you wish to check the point.

Notice that by using decimals in this fashion we can solve problems in which the divisor is larger than the dividend by the same techniques used when the dividend is larger than the divisor, and without bringing in ordinary fractions. Take the question of dividing 15 by 50. Without decimals we would have to say that $15 \div 50 = \frac{15}{50}$. We could reduce that fraction to lowest terms by dividing the numerator and denominator of the fraction by 5 so that the answer becomes $\frac{3}{10}$. (I will have something to say about reducing to lowest terms in the next chapter.)

On the other hand, why don't we write 15 as 15.0? Now, $150 \div 50 = 3$ — a problem we can solve at a glance. Therefore $15.0 \div 50 = 0.3$, a problem we can solve in the same glance. Since 0.3 is the decimal way of writing $\frac{3}{10}$, the answer is the same with and without decimals, but using decimals is certainly swifter. (There are times, to be sure, when fractions are easier and quicker than decimals. We'll get to such cases later on.)

Once again, the problem becomes a trifle more complicated when both divisor and dividend are decimals. What if, instead of $7.5 \div 15$, we have the problem $7.5 \div 1.5$ or $0.75 \div 0.00015$? Astonishingly enough, the situation in division is for once simpler than the corresponding situation in multiplication. Let's look at a few ordinary divisions using whole numbers only; $72 \div 12 = 6$, for instance. Suppose dividend and divisor are both divided by 3; we then have $24 \div 4 = 6$. What if the original numbers are both divided by 6? Then we have $12 \div 2 = 6$. What if they are both multiplied by 4? Then we have $288 \div 48 = 6$.

You can test as many cases as you like and you will find that if both dividend and divisor are multiplied (or divided) by the same number, the quotient remains the same; the answer to the problem is not affected.

Expressed in algebraic notation, we can say that $a \div b = a/b$. If a and b are both multiplied by n, the division becomes $an \div bn = an/bn = a/b$. If a and b are both divided by n then we have $a/n \div b/n$. This division is equivalent to $a/n \times n/b = an/bn = a/b$ once more. You may remember that we had a similar situation in subtraction, where the two numbers involved in the subtraction yielded the same difference when the same number was added to both or subtracted from both.

If now we are faced with a division in which dividend and divisor are both decimal numbers, we must try to convert the divisor to a whole number, since we can handle division by a whole number even when the dividend is a decimal. Consider the problem $7.5 \div 1.5$.

If we multiply the divisor (1.5) by 10, the decimal point moves one place to the right and 1.5 becomes 15. However, if we are to keep the quotient unchanged, the dividend must be multiplied by 10 also so that 7.5 becomes 75. The problem becomes $75 \div 15$ and the answer is 5.

If the problem were $0.75 \div 0.00015$, we would be faced with having to convert 0.00015 into a whole number. We could do this if we moved the decimal point five places to the right, which means multiplication by 100,000. In that case 0.00015 would become 15. But now we must also multiply 0.75 by 100,000 and move the decimal point five places to the right there, too. Don't be fooled into thinking that in 0.75 there are only two decimal places available. Remember that there is an unlimited reserve supply of zeros at the extreme right to the right of the decimal point. We can write 0.75 as 0.75000, and now when we move the decimal point five places to the right 0.75000 becomes 75,000. The problem $0.75 \div 0.00015$ becomes $75,000 \div 15$ and the answer is 5000.

Nor must you worry about multiplying or dividing by 10 or 100 or 100,000. Simply move the decimal point, remembering that, however you move it, you must move it exactly the same in dividend and divisor. And, in moving it, move it so that the divisor becomes a whole number. Then proceed as always.

This will work even if the dividend is itself a whole number to begin with. Thus, $75 \div 1.5$ becomes $750 \div$

15 if the decimal point is moved one place to the right in both dividend and divisor, and the answer, as you see at once, is 50.

So far, the decimal point has faced us with the problem of locating its correct position. With care, this is not much of a difficulty, but it does add to the chore of calculation. It is only fair, therefore, to ask if the decimal point in return can help us in our calculations and actually make things easier.

It does in one respect, we have already seen. Multiplication or division by numbers such as 10, 100, or 1000 can be accomplished by merely shifting the decimal point back and forth. Well, can we bend this to our purposes where numbers not of this sort are involved?

Actually we can. Suppose we want to multiply 68 by 5. This is not too hard, but we can introduce a time-saving step that will make it even easier. We could consider 5 as $10 \div 2$. Instead of saying 68×5, then, we can say $68 \times 10 \div 2$. By now you won't be the least surprised that a multiplication can be simplified by substituting two steps for one, and making one of the two steps a division besides. The two steps, naturally, are simple. To multiply by 10, we simply move the decimal point one place to the right. In the case of a whole number this is equivalent to adding a zero — 68 becomes 680. This is so easy that it scarcely counts as a step. The only comparison we need really make is whether it is simpler to multiply 68 by 5 or to divide 680 by 2. I think you will agree that dividing by 2 is simpler and that a glance is enough to tell us the answer: 340. Consequently, $68 \times 5 = 340$.

For somewhat larger numbers, the difference between the two methods is even more marked. Suppose you had to multiply 42.48 by 5. If you think of it as 424.8 divided by 2 you can see at once that $42.48 \times 5 = 212.4$.

If to multiply by 5 we multiply by 10 and divide by 2, then we do just the reverse in order to divide by 5. We divide by 10 and multiply by 2. (Since division is the inverse of multiplication, you would expect such opposites in behavior.) In order to divide 170 by 5, we divide by 10 first, which means shifting the decimal point one place to the left and changing 170 to 17. Which is easier now, $170 \div 5$ or 17×2? Clearly the latter, and the answer is 34.

We can carry this same principle to multiplications and divisions by some other numbers. For instance, $25 = 100 \div 4$. Why multiply by 25, then (something which would have to be done on paper by almost everyone), when we can multiply by 100 by simply moving the decimal point two places to the right and then divide by 4? Thus, 824×25 must, in the ordinary way, be worked out on paper. Yet consider that if one multiplies 824 by 100 to get 82,400 and then divides by 4, the answer, 20,600, appears without trouble. If in a particular case division by 4 is a bit clumsy, we can always divide by 2 twice. Accordingly, 7.56×25 can be rewritten as $756 \div 4$; and dividing by 2 twice gives us first 378, then 189; so $7.56 \times 25 = 189$.

Again we can reverse matters for division. Dividing by 25 is equivalent to dividing by 100 (moving the decimal point two places to the left), then multiplying by 4. If we are faced with $212 \div 25$, we change that to 2.12×4 and the answer comes out 8.48.

One further step brings us to 125, which is $1000 \div 8$. If we must multiply by 125, let us multiply by 1000 (moving the decimal point three places to the right) and divide by 8, or, if we choose, divide by 2 three times. Thus, 1.736×125 is the same as $1736 \div 8$. Dividing 1736 by 2 three times gives us 868, 434 and 217. Consequently, $1.736 \times 125 = 217$.

And the reverse? If we want the answer to $1311 \div 125$, first we divide by 1000, so 1311 becomes 1.311. The problem has become 1.311×8, and if we double 1.311 three times, 2.622, 5.244, and 10,488, the last figure — 10.488 — is the answer.

With very little extra trouble we can multiply by 15 or 35. The number 15 can be written as $10 + 5$; therefore, in multiplying by 15 we multiply first by 10, then by 5, and add the two products. In multiplying by 10 we merely move the decimal point one place to the right, and in multiplying by 5 we do the same thing and then divide by 2. The second product is half the size of the first. In other words, if we wish to solve 72×15, we add a zero to 72 (making it 720), take half of that

(360), and then add the two. As you see, $720 + 360 =$ 1080; so $72 \times 15 = 1080$.

To multiply by 35 is to multiply by $25 + 10$. Suppose we have 84×35. First we multiply 84×25, which becomes $8400 \div 4 = 2100$. Then we multiply 84 by 10, which is 840. Then we add 2100 and 840 to get 2940; so $84 \times 35 = 2940$. If you are afraid you'll forget 2100 while you're working with the 840, you can always jot down the 2100 after you get that part. Even with the time lost in jotting, you are still very likely to solve the problem more quickly than if you tried to do $84 \times$ 35 by the full method of multiplication.

This same procedure gives us an alternate method for multiplying by 125 without introducing division by 8. We can consider 125 as $25 + 100$. If we are faced with 76×125, we concentrate on 76×25. That is the same as $7600 \div 4$, which equals 1900. Next, $76 \times 100 = 7600$ and $7600 + 1900 = 9500$; thereby we find that $76 \times 125 = 9500$. And we have had to divide by 4 rather than 8.

It is scarcely any more trouble to multiply by a number very close to those for which such shortcuts are available. Suppose you had to multiply by 126 or 124. Well, $126 = 125 + 1$ and $124 = 125 - 1$. If you want to work with 76×126, and can find without too much trouble that $76 \times 125 = 9500$, you can add to that $76 \times$ 1, or 76 itself. Therefore, $76 \times 126 = 9576$.

If it were 76×124, you would subtract 76 from 9500. Therefore, $76 \times 124 = 9424$.

We have broken up multipliers into sums before now but we have never done so with divisors. Perhaps you may wonder why we don't. Since division is the reverse of multiplication, you may feel that instead of dividing by 35, we might divide first by 25 then by 10 and take the difference of the two quotients. This would be the exact reverse of the situation in multiplications. Nevertheless, *this does not work!*

Whenever you think of a possible shortcut — one you haven't seen suggested anywhere but which you've worked out from what seem to you to be general principles — always check it on some simple cases. If it doesn't work, forget it. Let me give you this case as an example.

If we wanted to solve 30×15 by adding 30×10 and 30×5, we would say $30 \times 15 = 300 + 150 = 450$. That is correct. Suppose, though, we wanted to say $30 \div 15$ was equal to $30 \div 10$ minus $30 \div 5$. If we tried that we would say $30 \div 15 = 3 - 6 =$ what? As we happen to know $30 \div 15 = 2$, but we certainly don't get 2 by trying to solve $3 - 6$.

Actually, instead of trying to say $3 - 6$, we could make each number the denominator of a fraction with 1 as the numerator, and then add. The addition would become $\frac{1}{3} + \frac{1}{6}$. We would find an answer to that with a unit numerator; in this case the answer is $\frac{1}{2}$; and the denominator, 2, is the answer we are seeking. This, obviously, is *not* a quick and easy method, and I certainly don't recommend it. Indeed, I urge you to forget

it; I have inserted this passage only as a horrible example.

Using algebraic notation to explain the above, we can
say this: if $b = c + d$, then $ab = a(c + d)$ and $a/b =
a/(c + d)$. But $ab = a(c + d)$ can be rewritten as
$ab = ac + ad$, which is fine and is what we do when we
convert a multiplier into a sum and multiply by augend
and addend separately. However, we *cannot* convert
$a/b = a(c + d)$ into $a/b = a/c + a/d$ or into $a/b =
a/c - a/d$ or anything of the sort. If we remove the
parentheses in $a/b = a(c + d)$ by correct algebraic
principles, we find we must say that

$$a/b = \frac{1}{b/a + c/a}$$

which gives us no handle for a decent shortcut.

Does this mean there is nothing to be done about
dividing by 15? Not at all. If you can't change a divisor
into the sum of smaller numbers, there is nothing
against changing it into the product of smaller numbers.
In fact, earlier in the book, I pointed out that $15 = 5 \times
3$, so that you can divide by 15 by first dividing by 3 and
then by 5 (or first by 5 and then by 3, if you prefer,
although it is usually better to divide by the smaller
number first).

Consider $765 \div 15$. We could divide by 3 first to get
255. Then divide by 5 to get 51.

Or we could decide to divide by 5 first, the short way.
Since $765 \div 5 = 76.5 \times 2$, the answer is 153. Divide

that by 3 and again the final answer is 51.

Still another way of handling this situation is to remember that a quotient is not changed by multiplying dividend and divisor by the same number. Therefore, if you double both 765 and 15, you will find that 765 ÷ 15 becomes 1530 ÷ 30. Next, divide both by 10 and you have 153 ÷ 3 = 51. In the same way, faced with 490 ÷ 35, you might double the dividend and divisor, making it 980 ÷ 70; divide both by 10, making it 98 ÷ 7; and the answer is 14.

How about multiplying by 55? Well, 55 is 5 + 50, and let's look at that for a moment. Since 50 is 5 × 10, this means that if we multiply by 5, then add a 0 to the answer (or, alternatively, move the decimal point one place to the right), we shall have the product we would have had if we had multiplied by 50. For instance, suppose we are dealing with 16.12 × 55. Let's first think of it as 16.12 × 5. That means multiply by 10, moving the decimal point one place to the right and then dividing by 2; and 161.2 ÷ 2 = 80.6. If we know that 16.12 × 5 = 80.6, then we also know that 16.12 × 50 = 806. It remains only to add 806 and 80.6 to get the final answer as 886.6.

We can also consider 55 as 11 × 5, multiplying 16.12 by 11 first and then by 5. I think that breaking up 55 into 5 + 50 is simpler in this case, but breaking it up into 11 × 5 may be simpler in other cases. You must keep an open mind about such things.

You can multiply by 44, or by 33, or by 66, or by 77,

using the same principle. Multiply by 4, shift the decimal place to give the product of a multiplication by 40, and add. Multiply by 3, shift the decimal place to give the product of a multiplication by 30, and add. And so on.

If you are willing to try subtracting you can multiply quickly by 45, for that is $50 - 5$. If you wanted to solve 16.12×45, you can still get the products of 16.12 with 5 and with 50, finding them to be 80.6 and 806. Now, however, you subtract: $806 - 80.6 = 725.4$, which is the product of 16.12×45.

In the same manner you can multiply by 27 (which is $30 - 3$), by 54 (which is $60 - 6$), and so on. And, of course, multiplying by 5.5 or by 0.45 or by 660 follows the same principles, with the added provision that you have to be careful about the location of the decimal point.

We can broaden the principle to take care of cases where matters aren't quite as simple as involving the mere movement of a decimal point.

Imagine that we wanted to multiply a number by 36. We already know that we can write 36 as 4×9 or as 6×6 or as $3 \times 3 \times 4$, or as $2 \times 2 \times 3 \times 3$, and make a series of multiplications with any of these combinations. However, there is still another device. Suppose we write 36 as $30 + 6$. Since 30 is five times as large as 6, any number multiplied by 30 will give a product five times as large as the same number multiplied by 6. Consequently, if you wanted to solve 132×36, you might first multiply 132 by 6 to get 792. Then multiply 792 by 5 by changing that to $7920 \div 2 = 3960$. Now you can add 3960 and 792 for the final answer of 4752.

You may think it easier to multiply by 6 and then multiply by 6 again, thus avoiding the addition. And, indeed, I think it is, in this case. Nevertheless, there may be other cases where treating 36 as $30 + 6$ — that is, $(5 \times 6) + 6$ — may be handy.

DOLLARS AND CENTS

Decimals are of particular importance to Americans, since American money is based on a decimal system. A large proportion of the calculations that Americans must make from day to day naturally involves money, and decimals are automatically involved.

The smallest American coin is the "cent," and one cent can be written 1¢, the cent symbol being a "c" with a line through it. The cent is sometimes called a "penny," but penny is the name of a small British coin (worth about $1\frac{1}{6}$ cents these days). The American use of the word is a hangover from Colonial times.

There are ten cents to the "dime" and ten dimes to the "dollar." A dime can be written as 10¢, therefore, and a dollar can be written as 100¢. The word "dollar" comes from the name of an old German coin, a *thaler*. This was a short form of *Joachimsthaler* and it was so called because it was coined in Joachimsthal, Bohemia. Joachimsthal in English would be "St. Joachim's Valley."

It is much more convenient to reckon in dollars than in cents, because most things cost a few dollars at least and you don't want to be dealing forever in hundreds or in thousands of cents. A dollar is therefore written with a special symbol of its own ($). This is a capital S with a vertical line through it or sometimes two vertical lines. The origin of this sign is unknown (though there are many theories, such as that originally it was "US" with the U printed over the S). The sign comes before the number, so that one dollar is written $1.

If we work with dollars, then a dime can be viewed as $\frac{1}{10}$ of a dollar, and a cent as $\frac{1}{100}$ of a dollar. (Indeed, the word "dime" comes from a Latin word meaning "tenths," while "cent" is from one meaning "hundredth.") Using the dollar symbol, then, a dime is $0.1 and a cent is $0.01. It is customary, in dealing with American money, always to allow two places after the decimal point, even when no odd number of cents are involved, so that the dime is always written as $0.10 when the dollar sign is used, and five dollars can be written $5.00.

In switching from the dollar symbol to the cent symbol we must move the decimal point two places to the right, since we are then multiplying by 100 ($1 = 100¢). In shifting from cents to dollars the decimal point must be moved two places to the left, because we are then dividing by 100 (100¢ = $1). Thus, $2.57 = 257¢ and 5298¢ = $52.98.

All coins other than the cent and the dime are forced

into this decimal system. The "half dollar" is, obviously, half a dollar. That makes it five dimes, or fifty cents, and it is written 50¢ or $0.50. The "quarter" is actually a short name for "quarter dollar," and it is two and a half dimes, or twenty-five cents. It is written 25¢ or $0.25. Finally, the "nickel" (so called because the metal nickel makes up a quarter of its substance, the rest being copper) is half a dime, or five cents. It can be written 5¢ or $0.05.

In calculating with American money it is not really necessary to worry about the different coins. To be sure, sometimes one tries to solve problems which may involve, for instance, the number of ways in which one can change a two-dollar bill without using nickels; but these problems are puzzles, and in this book we are not concerned with puzzles.

In serious calculations everything is done in dollars to the left of the decimal point and cents to the right of it. Even the dime is swallowed up, for $0.10 is never read "one dime" but always "ten cents." The sum $2.23 is not read "two dollars, two dimes, and three cents" but is read "two dollars and twenty-three cents." In fact, a common phrase representing money in the United States is "dollars and cents."

In calculating with American money, then, we follow all the rules for ordinary decimal numbers except that we must remember to keep the decimal point two places from the right at all times. Say that we want to multiply $2.51 by 10. The most convenient device would

be to move the decimal point one place to the right, so
the answer might be $25.1. However, the decimal point
is now only one place from the right. To make it two
places from the right (without actually moving it and
making the answer wrong), we add a zero from the
reserve supply on the extreme right and say $2.51 ×
10 = $25.10. If, instead, we multiply $2.51 by 100, the
answer is $251.00.

What if we divide $2.51 by 10? Now we must move
the decimal point one place to the left, and the quotient
will be $0.251. That final 1 represents a peculiarity,
however, for if we were to convert $0.251 to cents by
shifting the decimal point two places to the right we
would find the sum to be 25.1¢.

But there is no "tenth of a cent" in modern American
coinage. A tenth of a cent is sometimes called a "mill,"
from the Latin word for "thousandth," because a tenth
of a cent is a thousandth of a dollar. Tenths and even
hundredths of a cent are frequently used in business
calculations, but in ordinary day-to-day situations fractions of a cent are not used. If in any calculation a
fraction amounting to less than half a cent is met with,
it is simply dropped. If half a cent or a larger fraction
is met with, it is added to the answer as a whole cent:

$$\$2.51 \div 10 = \$0.25, \text{ and not } \$0.251$$
$$\$2.59 \div 10 = \$0.26, \text{ and not } \$0.259$$

PERCENTAGE

Decimals can help us with respect to percentages.
Percentages are themselves merely decimals in disguise,

and in a thoroughly unnecessary disguise, too.

It is often desirable in day-to-day life to deal with a small portion of a particular quantity as, for example, interest on a loan or discount on a sale. This small portion rises and falls as the quantity itself rises and falls. If the quantity triples, the small portion triples; if the quantity falls to a fifth of its original size, so does the small portion. In this way, the portion maintains a fixed relationship to the quantity.

Let us suppose that we are dealing with money and that the small portion is just $\frac{1}{100}$ of the quantity. Since a cent is $\frac{1}{100}$ of a dollar, this would mean that for every dollar in the sum, there is a cent in the small portion. You might offer that small sum as a discount to encourage prompt payment: "If you pay immediately, I will give you back a cent for every dollar you pay." Or you might charge one cent as interest for every dollar you lend: "When you pay back in three months, you must give me an additional cent for every dollar you pay back."

What applies to money would apply to anything else. For every hundred cents (that is, one dollar) one cent would make up the $\frac{1}{100}$ part. For every hundred dollars, one dollar would make up the $\frac{1}{100}$ part; for every hundred cats, one cat would make up the $\frac{1}{100}$ part. The small part would, in this case, be "one part of a particular thing out of every hundred parts of that particular thing." One could express this, shortly, as "one part per hundred."

This notion first arose in Roman times. In Latin, "per hundred" is *per centum*. This phrase was shortened (and sometimes joined together), becoming "per cent" in English. One part per hundred, therefore, is "one per cent." One per cent of 6 dollars (or 600 cents) is 6 cents. One per cent of 600 cats is 6 cats. One per cent of 5000 automobiles is 50 automobiles. In every case, you take $\frac{1}{100}$ of the sum, and that is one per cent. Since the 1400's the symbol % has stood for "per cent." It was originally a small *c* (for centum) with a little circle over it, thus, č, and you can see how that became %. Therefore, "one per cent" can be written as 1%.

Since 1%, or "one part per hundred," is actually equal to $\frac{1}{100}$, it can be written in decimal form as 0.01. In the same way, 6% is 0.06; 20% is 0.20 or 0.2, and 100% is 1.00 or 1. You can even have 154%, which is 1.54, or 1000%, which is 10.00 or simply 10. In short, any whole number written as a "per cent" can be changed into a decimal by simply placing a decimal point two places from the right and, of course, dropping the per cent sign.

Once a percentage is written as a decimal, it becomes very easy to handle. For instance 1% of 478 is simply $478 \times 0.01 = 4.78$. It also does not require much thought to see that 6% of 900 is 900×0.06, which is equivalent to $9 \times 6 = 54$.

You might wonder why we use percentages at all, if they are merely disguised decimals and if using decimals is so much simpler. The only answer to that is

that the ancient Romans made the first moves toward
the use of percentages, and these became better devel-
oped and more common throughout the Middle Ages.
Decimals did not come into use until the 1500's, and by
then percentages had been in use for a thousand years
and more and were so familiar that the business com-
munity has never been able to abandon them.

Sometimes percentages involve fractions, as in the
case of $7\frac{1}{2}\%$. The number $7\frac{1}{2}$ always means $7 + \frac{1}{2}$, so
$7\frac{1}{2}\%$ means $7\% + \frac{1}{2}\%$, and we have to ask ourselves
what $\frac{1}{2}\%$ means. Well, $1\% = 0.01$ and $\frac{1}{2}\%$ must be
half that. This means that $\frac{1}{2}\%$ is $0.01 \div 2$. If we write
0.01 as 0.010 (as we have every right to do), then
$0.010 \div 2 = 0.005$. This is equivalent to the fraction
$\frac{5}{1000}$ (as you can see if you divide 5 by 1000 — moving
the decimal point three places to the left and converting
5 to 0.005).

Since $\frac{1}{2}\%$ is 0.005, or $\frac{5}{1000}$, it can be spoken of as
"five parts per thousand." So, $7\frac{1}{2}\%$ is $0.07 + 0.005$, or
0.075, and it can be spoken of as either "seven and a half
parts per hundred" or as "seventy-five parts per thousand." Whatever it is called, it is most easily handled in
calculations if it is written in simple straightforward
decimal fashion as 0.075.

Very occasionally, people will speak of "parts per
thousand" as "per mill" (from the Latin word for "thousandth.)" In that case, the symbol $^0/_{00}$ may be used, so
that $7\frac{1}{2}\%$ could be spoken of as 75 per mill or written
$75\ ^0/_{00}$.

Then, too, chemical analysts might also speak of "parts per million" meaning one millionth, or $\frac{1}{1,000,000}$. Such "parts per million" can be abbreviated as "ppm."

All such "parts per" expressions can be easily written as decimals, thus:

One part in ten, equals $\frac{1}{10}$ or 0.1

One part in a hundred, equals $\frac{1}{100}$, 1 per cent, 1%, or 0.01

One part in a thousand equals $\frac{1}{1000}$, 1 per mill, $1\,^o/_{oo}$, or 0.001

One part in ten thousand equals $\frac{1}{10,000}$, or 0.0001

One part in a hundred thousand equals $\frac{1}{100,000}$, or 0.00001

One part in a million equals $\frac{1}{1,000,000}$, 1 ppm, or or 0.000001, and so on.

Notice that the number of zeros in the denominator of the fraction is one greater than the number to the right of the decimal point in the corresponding decimal. Thus, if you want to convert one ten-billionth to decimals, the process is simple. The fraction is $\frac{1}{10,000,000,000}$. There are ten zeros in the denominator, so there must be nine zeros to the right of the decimal point when it is written as a decimal. One ten-billionth is therefore 0.0000000001. To change that to a percentage, move the decimal point two places to the right and add the per cent sign, so that it becomes 0.00000001%.

Nor are we confined to "one part per —." Thus, six parts per thousand is six times as much as one part per thousand, or $6 \times 0.001 = 0.006$. Fifteen parts per hundred thousand is $15 \times 0.00001 = 0.00015$, and so on.

It is impossible to speak of "parts per — " where numbers like 100, and 1000 are not involved. One might speak of "six parts per fifteen" or "seventeen parts per twenty-five." This is just a way of describing a fraction. Just as "one part per hundred" equals $\frac{1}{100}$, so "six parts per fifteen" equals $\frac{6}{15}$ and "seventeen parts per twenty-five" equals $\frac{17}{25}$.

A practical example of this sort of thing is the expression "14 carat," which defines the purity of a particular gold alloy. The word "carat" is a way of saying "parts per twenty-four" so that 14 carat means "14 parts per 24." This really means that the alloy is $\frac{14}{24}$ gold.

But this brings us to fractions, which I have been bumping into now and then in the last two chapters, and I will delay further consideration until the next chapter.

CHECKING THE DECIMAL POINT

So far, I have discussed methods for checking answers obtained by each type of operation, but I have concentrated on the actual digits in the answer. The method of casting out nines, for instance, depends entirely on the digits and is unable to tell the wrong order of the digits from the right order.

Yet there is one way in which we can have all the digits correct and even in the right order, and *still* have an answer which is quite wrong. This happens when we misplace the decimal point or, which is the same thing, get the number of zeros in the answer wrong.

Of course, if we follow the methods of handling decimals in a sensible manner and keep our wits about us, we should not make mistakes in placing the decimal point. But then we should not make mistakes in digits either. The fact of the matter is that mistakes will happen and no matter how careful we are, a decimal point may slip out of place. Naturally, we can repeat the calculation but this is inefficient. It would be better if we found a different method.

Let's see the sort of problems in which the question of the position of the decimal place would chiefly arise. In addition or subtraction we are not likely to have trouble. There we line up the numbers with the decimal points in a vertical row and the answer has the decimal point also in that same row. It is in multiplication and division that misplacement of the decimal point is a problem.

Suppose you are multiplying 750 by 0.0000012. As far as digits are concerned you need only work it out as $75 \times 12 = 750 + 150 = 900$. You have the digit 9, therefore, but is it 0.0009 or 0.000009, or what? You may decide that the first alternative is correct by careful work, but are you sure? Is there any quick way of checking and being *certain?*

Again, what if you are dividing 123.2 by 0.11? In sheer digits, the answer is 112; but is it 1.12 or 11.2?

You are here interested not in the answer itself but merely in its "order of magnitude." Each shift of the decimal point by one place changes the number by one order of magnitude. This means that if one number is ten times as large as a second number it is also one order of magnitude greater. Thus 210 is one order of magnitude higher than 21 and it is one order of magnitude lower than 2100.

Nor need one be this exact. Numbers that differ by less than a multiple of 5 can be considered as of the same order of magnitude. For instance, 10 and 40 are of the same order of magnitude because the latter is only four times as large as the former. Again 125 and 217 are of the same order of magnitude, for the latter is less than twice the size of the former. However, 13 and 72 might fairly be considered one magnitude apart, for 72 is 6 times as large as 13.

Well, then, in a complicated multiplication, if one "rounds off" the numbers involved in such a way as not to alter any of the numbers by a multiple of more than 5, the chances are that although the digits of the new product will be altogether wrong, the order of magnitude will remain correct. If, in the new multiplication, the final answer, with the decimal point correctly placed, is easy to get, it serves as a guide for the original multiplication, for there the decimal point must be similarly placed.

Naturally, the smaller the change involved in rounding off, the more likely the order of magnitude is to remain correct. In a multiplication, furthermore, it is best to round off multiplicand and multiplier in opposite

directions, since this will introduce a smaller change in
the product than if multiplicand and multiplier are both
made larger or both smaller. (Remember that earlier
in the chapter, I explained that multiplying the multiplicand and dividing the multiplier by the same number
leaves the product unchanged.)

Let's return then to our multiplication problem of
750×0.0000012. We can increase the 750 slightly to
800 and decrease the 0.0000012 to 0.000001. The multiplication becomes 800×0.000001 and with such small
changes we can't possibly have altered the order of
magnitude of the product.

The new multiplication doesn't give us the correct
digits but it is easy to solve, decimal point and all. Let's
consider 800 as 8×100. Therefore the problem becomes $8 \times 100 \times 0.000001$. If we multiply $100 \times
0.000001$ first, the decimal point in the latter number
must be moved two places to the right, so that $100 \times
0.000001 = 0.0001$. That leaves us with $8 \times 0.0001 =
0.0008$, with no possibility of mistake in the position of
the decimal point.

The actual answer to the problem 750×0.0000012
contains the digit 9, not the digit 8, but the order of
magnitude must be the same. Therefore instead of
0.0008 we write 0.0009, and we can be quite certain
that we have the decimal point in the right place.

There is a possibility of error here that I must warn
you against by using a very simple case. Consider
0.95×0.09. If you think of digits alone, $95 \times 9 = 855$.

However, suppose you are not certain whether the actual answer to 0.95×0.09 is 0.855 or 0.0855. You decide to round off. Since 0.95 is almost 1 and 0.09 is almost 0.1, you can change the problem to read 1×0.1 without being much afraid of altering the order of magnitude. (It would be better if you altered multiplicand and multiplier in opposite directions, but the opportunity of using numbers like 1 and 0.1 is too attractive to give up.) Well, then $1 \times 0.1 = 0.1$ and that is the approximate answer.

If you take a quick look at 0.1 you might say "Aha, the digits start immediately to the right of the decimal point, without any zeros. Therefore 0.855 is right and 0.0855 is wrong."

Well, not so! If you compare 0.1 and 0.855 you see they are different orders of magnitude, for 0.855 is 8.55 times as large as 0.1. However, if you compare 0.1 and 0.0855, you see they are of the same order of magnitude, for 0.1 is only about $1\frac{1}{6}$ times as large as 0.0855. Therefore, the correct answer is 0.0855.

Always judge by the order of magnitude and not by the number of zeros alone.

Now let's pass on to division, where it is best to round off the numbers in the same direction, making the dividend and divisor both smaller or both larger. (Remember that if you multiply both dividend and divisor by the same number, or divide them by the same number, the quotient remains altogether unchanged.)

If we try $123.2 \div 0.11$, the division problem I men-

tioned earlier in this section, we can lower 123.2 to 120
and lower 0.11 to 0.1. Now the problem has become
$120 \div 0.1$. We have undoubtedly kept the order of
magnitude of the answer unchanged, but how much
simpler we have made the problem. If we multiply
both dividend and divisor by 10 now, we make the
problem simpler still, for it becomes $1200 \div 1 = 1200$.

We know that the answer in digits to $123.2 \div 0.11$ is
112, and now we know that its order of magnitude is
the same as that of 1200. The correct answer of the
original problem there is neither 1.12 nor 11.2 (two
possibilities I advanced earlier), but is 1120.

In fact, we can determine the order of magnitude of
an answer before we ever try to work it out. Suppose
we were faced with the problem:

$$\frac{78.99 \times 13.56}{167.11 \div 21.35}$$

By rounding off we can easily change the problem to

$$\frac{80 \times 10}{160 \div 20}$$

The second version will not give us exactly the right
answer but it will give us the order of magnitude and
in a second, too, for $80 \times 10 = 800$ and $160 \div 20 = 8$.
The fraction becomes $^{800}\!/_8$, which equals 100.

Now we can work out the problem with digits only
and never mind any of the decimal points at all. When
we do so we find that the answer in digits comes to

13684, plus a number of other digits which I will omit.
You know, however, the answer can't be 13.684 or 1368.4
because whatever it is, it must be of the same order
of magnitude as 100. The answer, therefore, is 136.84,
and you don't have to give two second's uneasiness to
whether the decimal point is in the right place or not.

THE USES OF APPROXIMATION

You will notice that, in working out the answer 136.84
to the problem with which I ended the previous section,
you spent a long time and ran an excellent chance of
making errors in the digits. However, in working out
the approximate answer, 100, you had no trouble at all,
spent virtually no time, and, indeed, probably did it in
your head.

The question has to arise: Must one spend all that
time and effort to get 136.84 when there are cases when
a simple 100 might do? Indeed, often a simple 100
would do. In making estimates, for instance, an approximate answer may be all we want. In making
actual measurements, we may not be able to be certain
of the exact fraction of an inch so that we *must* round
off our answers and no "exact" answer really makes
sense.

Early in the book, I pointed out methods for obtain-
ing approximate answers in addition; you now have the
method for multiplication. You round off the numbers
here as you did there.

Thus, 69×31 becomes 70×30, or 2100. Compare

that with the exact answer, 2139. Again, 7.89×3.15
becomes 8×3, or 24. Compare that with the exact
answer, 24.8535.

It is possible, of course, for numbers to be rounded
off in different fashions. Suppose you want to multiply
87 by 57. If you take the easy way out and raise both
numbers to get two multiples of ten with the smallest
possible change, you would have 90×60. The answer
to that is 5400 and you are quite a way off. The exact
answer is 4959 and your approximation, 5400, is about
16% too high.

Of course, it would have been worse if you had
lowered both numbers and made it $80 \times 50 = 4000$.
You would then be 20% too low.

But suppose you realized that in multiplication, multiplicand and multiplier should be changed in opposite
directions. If you raise the 87 to 90, you should, perhaps, lower the 57 to 50. You would then have $90 \times
50 = 4500$. This is better, but you are still more than
10% low.

However, you don't do that, you make the change
the other way. You raise the 57 to 60 and lower the 87
to 80. Now it is $80 \times 60 = 4800$ and you are only 3%
low.

Of course, you are not expected to be clairvoyant.
You may wonder how you can tell that changing
87×57 to 90×50 is not as good as changing it to
80×60. In both cases you are changing one number
by 3 and the other number by 7. Why, then, should

there be such a difference, and how can you know how to take advantage of the difference unless you know the correct answer in advance?

Actually, the reasoning is simple.

In general, the larger a number is, the larger the change it can take without too much damage to the answer. Consider the problem $1000 \times 10 = 10,000$. If you increase the multiplier, 10, by 10 to make it 20, you have $1000 \times 20 = 20,000$. You have doubled the answer. But suppose you increase the multiplicand, 1000, by 10 and make it 1010. Now 1010×10 is 10,100, an answer which is only 1% higher than the previous answer.

So let's go back to 87×57. If we round it off to 90×50, we have changed the larger number by 3 and the smaller number by 7. If we round it off to 80×60, we have changed the larger number by 7 and the smaller number by 3. All we need do is remember that the larger number can better absorb the larger change and we will automatically choose 80×60 as the better method of rounding.

Divisions can also be rounded off to give quick though possibly not entirely accurate answers. In the case of division, remember to make the changes in the same direction, giving the larger number the greater change, if possible. Thus, $78.408 \div 26.4$ can be rounded off to $75 \div 25 = 3$. This is an excellent approximation, achieved in a second, for the correct answer is 2.97.

Again, suppose you are faced with $160.906 \div 43$.

Your first impulse might be to round it off to $160 \div 40$ and give yourself an answer of 4. That isn't too bad, but 160.906 is approximately four times as large as 43 and it can take a change that is approximately four times as large. If you reduce 43 by 3 to 40, then 160.906 ought to be reduced to 150 rather than 160. A change of 11 for the larger number is more in keeping with the change in 3 for the lower number. The problem $150 \div 40$ can be changed to $15 \div 4$ by dividing both dividend and divisor by 10, and the answer is $3\frac{3}{4}$, or 3.75.

The actual answer for $160.906 \div 43$ is 3.742, and you see that 3.75 is a very good approximation indeed, much better than 4 would have been. Compare the time it takes to get the 3.75 by approximation and the 3.742 by long division and ask yourself if there are not times when the saving in time is worth the trifling inaccuracy.

The use of approximations also makes it possible to work out quick ways for dividing by prime numbers greater than 10. The price you pay, once again, is a trifling inaccuracy.

Suppose, for instance, you must divide a number by 17. Now $17 \times 6 = 102$. That product is almost equal to 100, so suppose you pretend it *is* equal to 100. In that case, instead of dividing by 17 (long division for sure), divide by 100, by moving the decimal point two places to the left and then multiply by 6.

As an example, consider $134.3 \div 17$. Change that to $134.3 \div 100 \times 6 = 1.343 \times 6 = 8.058$. Compare this with the correct answer, which you would find by long division to be 7.9.

Now here is something I don't particularly recommend for beginners, but as one gets used to this way of handling numbers by approximations, one can see how to correct the approximate answers you get in order to come closer to the true answer.

The approximate answer you get for division by 17, when you divide by 100 and multiply by 6, comes out a little too high. The reason for this is that $17 \times 6 = 102$ and you should, for complete accuracy, have divided by 102 and not by 100. By dividing by the smaller number, you get a higher quotient. The difference between 100 and 102 is 2%. Therefore, reduce your approximate quotient by 2% to correct for the error. This isn't hard. Since 1% of 8.058 is 0.08058, which you can round off to 0.08, 2% of 8.058 would be twice that, or 0.16. Now, then, round off 8.058 to 8.06 and carry through the correcting subtraction: $8.06 - 0.16$ gives you 7.9 which, as it happens, is exactly the correct answer.

Once you are familiar with the method, division by 100 followed by multiplication by 6 followed by subtraction of 2% of the approximate quotient will still take you less time than long division by 17.

Similarly, consider division by 13. Since $13 \times 8 = 104$, you can get an approximate answer by dividing by 100 and multiplying by 8. If you want to improve the approximation, you can subtract 4% of the quo-

tient's value from the quotient. An alternative is to
divide by 200 and multiply by 15, since $13 \times 15 = 195$.
Here you are dividing by 200, which is a bit more than
2% larger than the correct value of 195. Your approximate quotient will be a bit more than 2% smaller than
the true value and you can make the proper correction.

If you wish to divide by 19, you can round that figure
off to 20 and convert the division into a simple one
indeed. The divisor as rounded off would be higher
than the true number by about 5%, so the quotient will
be too low by about 5% and can be corrected upward.

To divide 1368 by 19, write it $1368 \div 20 = 684 \div
10 = 68.4$. To get 5% of that quotient we must solve
68.4×0.05. Since you are only after an approximation,
you can round this off to 70×0.05, or 7×0.5, which
equals 3.5. (In a multiplication, if you divide the multiplicand by 10 you must multiply the multiplier by 10
to keep the product unchanged; therefore $70 \times 0.05 =
7 \times 0.5$).

If you now add 68.4 and 3.5, you have the sum 71.9.
If you work out the correct answer to $1368 \div 19$ by long
division you come out with 72.

You can work up a variety of methods for handling
difficult prime divisors, but you must be careful. It is
all too easy to work out a fascinating method that includes so many steps and corrections that it would be
a relief to go back to long division. Remember that the
prime aim of such methods is not to display how in-
genious one is, but to save time and labor.

7

Fractions

A fraction is an expression of the form a/b, in which a, the number above the horizontal line, is the "numerator" and b, the number below the horizontal line, is the "denominator." Such a fraction actually represents a division, with a the dividend and b the divisor so that a/b is equal to $a \div b$.

For this reason, the expression $^{16}\!/_4$ is identical with $16 \div 4$ and this is equal to 4. In the same way $^{30}\!/_{15} = 2$, $^{12}\!/_2 = 6$, and so on. Such fractions, in which the numerator is larger than the denominator, are examples of "improper fractions."

Where the numerator is smaller than the denominator, as in $^1\!/_3$, $^2\!/_5$, $^4\!/_7$, there is no whole number obtained by the division. Such fractions are examples of "proper fractions."

Sometimes a fraction may have a numerator which, although larger than the denominator, is not divisible by the denominator. An example is the improper fraction $^{31}\!/_7$. This represents $31 \div 7$, which, if one conducts division in the usual manner, gives the answer $4^3\!/_7$. You might also tell yourself that $^{31}\!/_7 = {}^{28}\!/_7 + {}^3\!/_7$. Since $^{28}\!/_7 = 4$, $^{31}\!/_7 = 4 + {}^3\!/_7$. When a whole number and a fraction are added it is customary simply to run them together thus: $4\frac{3}{7}$.

An expression such as $4\frac{3}{7}$, containing both a whole number and a fraction, is called a "mixed number."

Earlier in the book, I pointed out that dividing both dividend and divisor by the same number does not change the quotient. Suppose we have the improper fraction $\frac{48}{24}$. Its value is 2. If we divide the numerator (dividend) and denominator (divisor) of that fraction, each by 2, we have $\frac{24}{12}$, which also has the value 2. We can continue the process, dividing by 2 again, by 2 still again, and finally by 3, and at each stage the value of the fraction we get, $\frac{12}{6}$, $\frac{6}{3}$, and $\frac{2}{1}$, will be 2. All these fractions are equal.

Notice that $\frac{2}{1} = 2$. Any fraction which has a denominator of 1 has a value equal to its numerator, since division of a number by 1 gives that number itself as a quotient. Hence $\frac{3}{1} = 3$, $\frac{17}{1} = 17$, $\frac{561}{1} = 561$, and so on. Working the other way, any whole number can be made into a fraction by placing it over 1 as a denominator. You can put 75 into fractional form by writing it $\frac{75}{1}$, and so on.

Proper fractions also retain their value if numerator and denominator are both divided by the same number. Thus, $\frac{17}{34}$ can be divided, top and bottom, by 17 to give the fraction $\frac{1}{2}$, which has the same value as $\frac{17}{34}$. The fraction $\frac{8}{10}$ can be set equal to $\frac{4}{5}$ after division, top and bottom, by 2. The fraction $\frac{6}{20} = \frac{3}{10}$, $\frac{7}{21} = \frac{1}{3}$, $\frac{14}{24} = \frac{7}{12}$, and so on.

This process can be continued until there are no whole numbers left which will divide both numerator and denominator and yield whole number quotients. No whole number will divide both numerator and denominator to give whole-number quotients in the case of such fractions as $\frac{1}{2}$, $\frac{2}{3}$, $\frac{3}{4}$, $\frac{5}{7}$, $\frac{19}{75}$, and so on. Such fractions are said to be "reduced to lowest terms."

In working with fractions, it is common to use them after they have been reduced to lowest terms, because then we are working with the smallest numbers possible. Why try to deal with $\frac{20}{60}$ when we can just as well deal with $\frac{1}{3}$?

In adding and subtracting fractions, it is necessary to keep the denominators the same throughout. Thus (and I will use words to make the situation clearer), one fifth plus one fifth equals two fifths ($\frac{1}{5} + \frac{1}{5} = \frac{2}{5}$), just as one apple plus one apple equals two apples. Again, seven twenty-fifths minus three twenty-fifths equals four twenty-fifths ($\frac{7}{25} - \frac{3}{25} = \frac{4}{25}$) just as seven oranges minus three oranges equal four oranges.

However, one fifth cannot be added to seven twenty-fifths directly, or subtracted from it directly, any more than you can add one apple to (or subtract one apple from) seven oranges. What would your answer be if you tried?

Fortunately, although one cannot change apples into oranges or oranges into apples, numbers at least can be manipulated. Fifths can be changed into twenty-fifths and twenty-fifths can be changed into fifths.

Suppose we are indeed faced with the problem $\frac{1}{5}$ + $\frac{7}{25}$. We cannot work out the sum unless we make both denominators equal. To change $\frac{7}{25}$ into fifths, we must divide the denominator by 5. In order to keep the value of the fraction unchanged we must also divide the numerator by 5, but $7 \div 5$ does not yield a whole number as quotient, and this introduces complications. In fact division only rarely yields a whole number, so, on the whole, it is not wise to try to change a fraction by division without a close inspection of the fraction first.

On the other hand, if we want to change $\frac{1}{5}$ into twenty-fifths we have to multiply the denominator by 5 and, of course, the numerator also, to keep the value of the fraction unchanged. Fortunately, the multiplication of any whole number by any whole number gives a whole-number product every time. There will therefore never be complications in multiplying the numerator and denominator of a fraction by any number.

The fraction $\frac{1}{5}$, multiplied by 5 top and bottom, becomes $\frac{5}{25}$. Therefore, $\frac{1}{5} + \frac{7}{25}$ can be written $\frac{5}{25} + \frac{7}{25}$ and, now that we have both fractions with the same denominator, the answer is $\frac{12}{25}$. In the same way, $\frac{3}{4} - \frac{1}{2} = \frac{3}{4} - \frac{2}{4} = \frac{1}{4}$.

This same system can be used for mixed numbers, too. If you must work out $3\frac{1}{4} + 4\frac{4}{5}$, you might first change both numbers into improper fractions. The whole number 3 can be written as $\frac{3}{1}$ and if both numerator and denominator are multiplied by 4, it becomes $\frac{12}{4}$. Since $3\frac{1}{4}$ is the same as $3 + \frac{1}{4}$, that can now be written as $1\frac{2}{4} + \frac{1}{4} = 1\frac{3}{4}$. In the same way, $4\frac{2}{5}$ becomes $\frac{4}{1} + \frac{2}{5} = \frac{20}{5} + \frac{2}{5} = 2\frac{2}{5}$.

Now the problem $3\frac{1}{4} + 4\frac{2}{5}$ becomes $1\frac{3}{4} + 2\frac{2}{5}$ and we face the further task of adjusting the denominators. The 4 can't be changed into a 5 by multiplication, nor can the 5 be changed into 4. If you think a little, however, you will see that the 5 can be changed into 20 by multiplication by 4, while the 4 can be changed into 20 by multiplication by 5. Consequently we multiply both the numerator and denominator of $1\frac{3}{4}$ by 5 to get $\frac{65}{20}$. Then we multiply both the numerator and denominator of $2\frac{2}{5}$ by 4 to get $\frac{96}{20}$. Now we find we have $\frac{65}{20} + \frac{96}{20} = \frac{161}{20}$, and that is the answer. If we would rather not leave it as an improper fraction, we can write it as $161 \div 20$ and find the answer to be $8\frac{1}{20}$. Sticking to mixed numbers throughout, we can say $3\frac{1}{4} + 4\frac{2}{5} = 8\frac{1}{20}$.

FRACTIONS AND DECIMALS

The addition and subtraction of fractions and of mixed numbers requires complicated manipulations, and it is no wonder that youngsters, first introduced to fractions, take a dislike to them. Is there any way of getting around them?

In certain cases, yes. There are some fractions which can be converted into simple decimals, and for decimals one need not worry about any of the contortions involved in the addition and subtraction of fractions. Whole-number devices are good enough.

Of course, we know that $\frac{1}{10}$ can be written as 0.1, $\frac{3}{10}$, as 0.3, $\frac{1}{100}$ as 0.01, and so on. However, decimals can be obtained even for fractions where the denominator is not 10, 100, 1000 or any of this type of number. For instance, $\frac{1}{2}$ can be written $1 \div 2$. Well, then, what if you write 1 as 1.0, as it is perfectly all right to do? In that case $1.0 \div 2 = 0.5$ and we can therefore say that $\frac{1}{2} = 0.5$

Since $1\frac{1}{2}$ is actually $1 + \frac{1}{2}$, we can write it as $1 + 0.5$ or as 1.5. In the same way, $7\frac{1}{2} = 7.5$, $18\frac{1}{2} = 18.5$, $239\frac{1}{2} = 239.5$, and so on. In the same way $\frac{1}{5}$ is $1 \div 5$, which can be written as $1.0 \div 5$, which equals 0.2. Therefore, $\frac{1}{5} = 0.2$, $17\frac{1}{5} = 17.2$, $87\frac{1}{5} = 87.2$, and so on.

What about $\frac{2}{5}$? You can work this out in either of two ways. First, $\frac{2}{5} = 2.0 \div 5 = 0.4$. Second, $\frac{2}{5} = 2 \times \frac{1}{5} = 2 \times 0.2 = 0.4$. In either case, $\frac{2}{5} = 0.4$. You can also show very easily that $\frac{3}{5} = 0.6$ and $\frac{4}{5} = 0.8$. Furthermore, $24\frac{3}{5} = 24.6$, $2\frac{2}{5} = 2.4$, $10\frac{4}{5} = 10.8$, and so on.

You see, then, that one advantage of putting fractions into decimal form is that proper fractions, improper fractions, and mixed numbers all melt into ordinary numbers containing a decimal point.

Halves and fifths come out as simple decimals because our number system is based on 10 and 10 is divisible by 2 and by 5. This means that any fraction with a denominator which can be expressed as a product of 2's and 5's can be converted into a simple decimal.

Consider $\frac{1}{4}$, for instance, where the denominator $4 = 2 \times 2$. The fraction $\frac{1}{4}$ can be expressed as $1.00 \div 4$, or 0.25. The fraction $\frac{2}{4}$ is $2.00 \div 4$ or 0.5. Here, then, we have another advantage of the decimal form: $\frac{2}{4} = 0.5$ and $\frac{1}{2} = 0.5$. For that matter, if you work out $\frac{17}{34}$ ($17.00 \div 34$) or $\frac{29}{58}$ ($29.00 \div 58$), you will find that their value is 0.5 also. And, of course, $\frac{5}{10} = 0.5$ also. Any fraction that reduces to $\frac{1}{2}$ as its lowest terms equals 0.5. The decimal 0.5 represents not only $\frac{1}{2}$ but a whole family of fractions. In decimals it is not necessary ever to reduce to lowest terms, because all are adjusted to tenths, hundredths, thousandths, etc., to begin with.

And $\frac{3}{4}$? That is equal to $\frac{2}{4} + \frac{1}{4}$, which is to say, to $0.5 + 0.25$, or 0.75. So $\frac{3}{4} = 0.75$.

Where the denominator of a fraction is 8 ($2 \times 2 \times 2$), 10 (2×5), 16 ($2 \times 2 \times 2 \times 2$), 20 ($2 \times 2 \times 5$), 25 ($5 \times 5$), and so on, simple decimals can be found. For instance, $\frac{1}{8} = 0.125$. Therefore, $\frac{3}{8} = 0.375$, $\frac{5}{8} = 0.625$, and $\frac{7}{8} = 0.875$.

Then, too, $\frac{1}{10} = 0.1$, $\frac{1}{16} = 0.0625$, $\frac{1}{20} = 0.05$, $\frac{1}{25} = 0.04$, and so on. Based on this, $\frac{7}{20} = 0.05 \times 7 = 0.35$, $\frac{9}{25} = 9 \times 0.04 = 0.36$, $8\frac{7}{20} = 8.35$, $11\frac{9}{25} = 11.36$, and so on.

If you form the habit of converting such fractions into decimals whenever you use them, you will eventually memorize the conversions and have no difficulty. When you see $\frac{5}{8}$, you will automatically think 0.625; $\frac{3}{5}$ will be an instant 0.6; $19\frac{1}{20}$ an obvious 19.05, and so on.

The gains to be derived are considerable. You can

add and subtract fractions in decimal form without worrying about converting mixed numbers into improper fractions and without worrying about adjusting denominators. Instead of going through a great deal of complication in deciding that $3\frac{1}{4} + 4\frac{4}{5} = 8\frac{1}{20}$, as we did in the previous section, we simply write $3\frac{1}{4}$ as 3.25 and $4\frac{4}{5}$ as 4.8. Now, 3.25 + 4.8 (remembering to keep the decimal point lined up) is 8.05. You can write this as $8\frac{1}{20}$ if you wish, but usually there is no reason why you should. The sum, which required great pains in mixed number form, becomes an easy mental addition in decimals.

To give another example, consider $8\frac{7}{25} - 5\frac{5}{8}$ and, working with fractions strictly, see how long it takes you to come up with the answer (which happens to be $2\frac{131}{200}$.) Now, remember that $\frac{7}{25}$ is $7 \times \frac{1}{25}$, or 7×0.04 and therefore 0.28, while $\frac{5}{8}$ is 0.625. Therefore, $8\frac{7}{25} - 5\frac{5}{8}$ is equal to 8.28 − 5.625 and almost at once you get the answer 2.655, which, as you can easily check for yourself, is equal to $2\frac{131}{200}$.

There is no question that working in decimals wherever possible will greatly reduce the time required in adding and subtracting fractions.

Why, then, do people insist on using fractions at all? Well, there are several reasons. In the first place, fractions were invented far back at the dawning of civilization and were used by the ancient Babylonians and Egyptians, who worked out complicated methods for handling them. The tradition of fractions is therefore a very strong and ancient one, whereas the use of decimals is only about 500 years old.

Secondly, fractions are sometimes more convenient than decimals — perhaps not in addition and subtraction, but certainly, as we shall soon see, in multiplication and division.

Thirdly, not all fractions can be placed into really simple decimal form. Only those with denominators that can be expressed as products of twos and fives can.

Consider $\frac{1}{3}$, for instance. This is $1.0 \div 3$, but if you try to carry through the division you will find that there is no end to the decimal you get. The fraction $\frac{1}{3}$ is equal to 0.333333 . . . with the threes going on forever. Try $\frac{1}{6}$ and you get 0.166666666 . . . , while $\frac{1}{9}$ is 0.11111111111 . . .

These are "repeating decimals," in which a figure or group of figures repeats itself over and over. As an example, where the repeating group consists of more than one digit, $\frac{1}{11}$ is 0.0909090909 . . . where the repeating group contains two digits. And $\frac{1}{7}$ is 0.142857142857142857142857 . . . , where the repeating group contains six digits.

Working with repeating decimals is by no means as neat as working with small definite fractions. For instance, $\frac{1}{7} + \frac{1}{11}$ can be solved after the problem is written as $\frac{11}{77} + \frac{7}{77}$, which gives the answer $\frac{18}{77}$. It may take you a few moments to see that $\frac{1}{7}$ and $\frac{1}{11}$ can both be put into fractions with the denominator 77, work out the proper numerators, then carry through the addition. Still, that is surely better than to try to add 0.142857142857142857 . . . and 0.09090909090909 . . . The answer to such an addition of repeating decimals happens to be 0.233766233766233766 . . . another repeating decimal in which the repeating group is made up of six digits. You might well prefer the answer $18/77$ to that repeating decimal. I would.

MULTIPLICATION OF FRACTIONS

Although multiplication and division are usually considered more complicated procedures than addition and subtraction, the multiplication and division of fractions is actually easier than the addition and subtraction of fractions. In multiplying or dividing fractions, we don't have to worry about any differences in the denominator. We can take the fractions exactly as they are and multiply (or divide) numerator by numerator and denominator by denominator. It is better to have the fractions in their lowest terms while you are working, so that you are dealing with the smallest possible numbers, but that is only for convenience.

In algebraic notation: $a/b \times c/d = ac/bd$ and $a/b \div c/d = \dfrac{a/c}{b/d}$. Thus, $2/5 \times 1/4 = 2/20$, which you can quickly reduce to $1/10$. Again, $7/8 \div 1/2 = 7/4$, which can also be expressed $1\frac{3}{4}$. In decimal form, these problems would be $0.4 \times 0.25 = 0.1$ and $0.875 \div 0.5 = 1.75$. In the first case, the decimal form of the problem is about as simple as the fractional form, but in the latter case the fractional form is definitely the simpler; at least, in my opinion.

Then, suppose you are considering $2/7 \times 5/6$. The answer, you can see at a glance, is made up of $2 \times 5 = 10$ in the numerator and $7 \times 6 = 42$ in the denominator. The answer is therefore $10/42$ or, reducing to lowest terms, $5/21$. If you tried the same problem in decimal form: $2/7 = 0.285714285714285714 \ldots$ and $5/6 = 0.8333333333333 \ldots$, and surely you wouldn't want to multiply these numbers.

In the same way, $15/49 \div 5/7 = 3/7$, a solution difficult to reach if you put $15/49$ and $5/7$ into decimal form.

In multiplications and divisions involving fractions, then, we will usually want to stick to fractions and we may as well look closely at them in order to see how best to handle them. Let's consider the problem $8 \times \frac{1}{2}$. In order not to get confused by trying to deal with both whole numbers and fractions, let's write the whole number in fraction form, too, so that we can express the problem as $8/1 \times \frac{1}{2}$. If we multiply these two fractions, numerator by numerator and denominator by denominator, we get the answer $8/2$, which can also be written $8 \div 2$, or, in fractional form, $8/1 \div 2/1$.

We reach the conclusion, then, that $8/1 \times \frac{1}{2}$ can also be written $8/1 \div 2/1$.

Suppose, next, we try the problem $8 \div \frac{1}{2}$, or, in fractional form, $8/1 \div \frac{1}{2}$. We know that the quotient won't be changed if we multiply both dividend and divisor by 2, so we can make the problem $16/1 \div 2/2$. In whole numbers, $^{16}\!/_1 = 16$ and $^2\!/_2 = 1$, so that $8 \div \frac{1}{2}$ becomes $16 \div 1$ and the answer to that is 16. We conclude then that $^8\!/_1 \div \frac{1}{2} = 16$. However, $^8\!/_1 \times ^2\!/_1 = ^{16}\!/_1$, or 16. Therefore we end by saying that $^8\!/_1 \div \frac{1}{2}$ can also be written $^8\!/_1 \times ^2\!/_1$.

Now when a fraction is turned upside down so that the numerator becomes the denominator and the denominator becomes the numerator, the two fractions are said to be "reciprocals" of each other. Thus, $^2\!/_5$ is the reciprocal of $^5\!/_2$, and vice versa; $^{17}\!/_{12}$ is the reciprocal of $^{12}\!/_{17}$, and vice versa. Again, $^5\!/_1$ is the reciprocal of $\frac{1}{5}$, and vice versa. Since fractions with a denominator of 1 are almost always written as whole numbers, we can perfectly well say that 5 is the reciprocal of $\frac{1}{5}$, and vice versa; 2 is the reciprocal of $\frac{1}{2}$, and vice versa; $\frac{1}{12}$ is the reciprocal of 12, and vice versa, and so on.

(The only exceptional case is 1, which is its own reciprocal, since $\frac{1}{1}$, turned upside down, is still $\frac{1}{1}$. Of course, $^2\!/_2$ is its own reciprocal and so are $^5\!/_5$, $^8\!/_8$, $^{343}\!/_{343}$, and so on. All these fractions, however, are but different ways of writing 1.)

Well, suppose we say once again that $^8\!/_1 \times \frac{1}{2} = ^8\!/_1 \div ^2\!/_1$ (and find similar situations in as many different cases as we care to test). We can say that if two fractions are multiplied, one can get the same answer if one of the fractions is made into its reciprocal and the multiplication is converted into a division. By the same token, if one fraction is divided by another and if the divisor is converted into its reciprocal, then the division becomes a multiplication and the same answer is obtained.

Thus, if we are faced with $^{11}/_{17} \times ^{5}/_{12}$, we can, if we choose, express it as $^{11}/_{17} \div ^{12}/_{5}$. Again, $^{4}/_{9} \div ^{2}/_{3}$ can be written $^{4}/_{9} \times ^{3}/_{2}$. In algebraic symbolism we can say that $a/b \div c/d = a/b \times d/c$. And $a/b \times c/d = a/b \div d/c$.

In general, multiplication is simpler than division; therefore every division involving fractions ought automatically be turned into a multiplication by converting the divisor into its reciprocal. We can consequently confine our attention to multiplication only.

Suppose, for instance, we had the problem $^{5}/_{16} \div ^{5}/_{9}$. If we tried to divide directly, we would have to divide the numerator by the numerator and the denominator by the denominator. We cannot, however, always rely on division to give us whole numbers. To be sure, $5 \div 5 = 1$, but $16 \div 9$ gives us $1^{7}/_{9}$ and to write the answer

as $\dfrac{1}{1^{7}/_{9}}$ would not be helpful.

So we "invert." We convert $^{5}/_{9}$ to its reciprocal $^{9}/_{5}$, and also convert the division to a multiplication, so that $^{5}/_{16} \div ^{5}/_{9}$ becomes $^{5}/_{16} \times ^{9}/_{5}$. Multiplication of whole numbers will always yield a whole number, and the answer is $^{45}/_{80}$. To reduce it to lowest terms, we see that both 45 and 80 are divisible by 5. Dividing top and bottom of the fraction by 5, we find it can be expressed as $^{9}/_{16}$. Since 9 and 16 have no factors in common, the fraction can be reduced no further.

It is possible to reduce fractional products to lowest terms before actually carrying through the multiplication of fractions. By doing so you will save time.

If you were multiplying $15/14$ by $21/55$, the answer would be $315/770$. Both $15/14$ and $21/55$ are in lowest terms, but $315/770$ is not. Since both 315 and 770 end in 5 or 0, both are divisible by 5. Dividing numerator and denominator by 5, we can change $315/770$ to $63/154$. We might wonder quite a while whether 63 and 154 had any common factors and we might not even see that both were divisible by 7, and consider $63/154$ to be in its lowest terms.

However, if we go back to the problem $15/14 \times 21/55$, it doesn't matter whether, in multiplying the denominators, we say 14×55 or 55×14 (since $ab = ba$). Consequently, we might just as well reverse the denominators and write the problem $15/55 \times 21/14$, for we would get the same answer.

But now the fractions we are working with are clearly not in lowest terms. There is the common factor 5 in 15 and 55, so $15/55$ becomes $3/11$; and there is a common factor 7 which clearly makes $21/14$ into $3/2$. So the problem becomes $3/11 \times 3/2$ and the answer is $9/22$. We have no trouble in seeing that $9/22$ is in its lowest terms.

Why does it matter whether we reduce the fractions to lowest terms before multiplying or after? Simply that after multiplication both numerator and denominator are larger numbers and the larger the numbers the harder it is to spot common factors quickly, especially where the common factor is 7, 11, 13, or some other number for which no simple rule for divisibility is established.

In fact, there is no necessity for switching denominators in such cases. You can just divide through by common factors in any of the numerators and any of the denominators in fractions being multiplied. Thus, in $\frac{5}{16} \times \frac{9}{5}$ you can divide the first numerator and the second denominator by 5, so that the problem becomes $\frac{1}{16} \times \frac{9}{1}$ and the answer is $\frac{9}{16}$.

This process of dividing the numerator and denominator of fractions being multiplied by common factors contains a trap. It won't work for fractions being added or subtracted! It will work *only* in multiplication. (It won't even work in just this way in the division of fractions, but a division of fractions can always be converted into a multiplication and then it will work.)

Naturally, in the multiplication of fractions, all the shortcuts available for multiplication generally can be used. If you are trying to handle $7\frac{1}{5} \times 1\frac{1}{5}$ (without changing them into decimals) you can see at a glance that there are no cancellations possible. You must multiply numerator by numerator and denominator by denominator without the ability to simplify matters by reducing the numbers.

Well, then, $71 \times 11 = 710 + 71 = 781$, and the product is therefore $^{781}\!/_{25}$. This is $781 \div 25$ or 7.81×4. Doubling 7.81 twice, we have 15.62; 31.24, and it is 31.24 that is the answer.

If we want the answer as an improper fraction, we can regard it as $31^{24}\!/_{100}$ or $^{31}\!/_1 + ^{24}\!/_{100}$ or $^{3100}\!/_{100} + ^{24}\!/_{100}$ or $^{3124}\!/_{100}$. Reduced to lowest terms, this becomes (after dividing both numerator and denominator by 4) $^{781}\!/_{25}$, or, in mixed-number form, $781 \div 25 = 31^6\!/_{25}$.

FRACTIONS AND PERCENTAGE

Sometimes it is convenient to consider percentages as fractions rather than as decimals. Suppose you are interested in determining 25% of 16. (The word "of" in such a phrase is usually taken to mean multiplication, so that "half of three" means "$\frac{1}{2} \times 3$.") In order to solve the problem $25\% \times 16$, we might convert the percentage to a decimal by moving the decimal point two places to the left and dropping the per cent sign. Thus, 25% would become 0.25 and the problem would be 0.25×16. We can multiply 16 by 25 by first multiplying 16 by 100 (to get 1600) and then dividing by 4 to get 400. If we place the decimal point in the product as it is in the multiplicand (two places from the right), we end with our answer, which is 4.00, or 4.

However, we should know that 0.25 is, in fractional terms, $\frac{1}{4}$ and that therefore $25\% = \frac{1}{4}$. Instead of $25\% \times 16$, we write $\frac{1}{4} \times 16$, and we see at once that the answer is $^{16}\!/_4$ or 4.

In the same way, $50\% = \frac{1}{2}$, $10\% = \frac{1}{10}$, $75\% = \frac{3}{4}$, $0\% = \frac{4}{5}$, and $12\% = \frac{3}{25}$. For that matter, $13\% =$

$^{13}\!/_{100}$ and $23\% = {}^{23}\!/_{100}$. Any percentage can be converted into a fraction.

You can't always be sure which is the easier technique, to convert the percentage to a decimal or to a fraction. It depends on the problem. If you have both the decimal and fractional equivalent of a percentage at your fingertips, however, you are free to make your choice.

Suppose you have a fractional percentage; let us say $12\frac{1}{2}\%$. You can convert the $\frac{1}{2}$ to a decimal before doing anything else to the percentage. In other words $12\frac{1}{2}\% = 12.5\%$. Now convert the whole expression to decimal form by moving the decimal point two places to the left, so that $12.5\% = 0.125$, which is, in turn, equal to $\frac{1}{8}$. Therefore $12\frac{1}{2}\% = \frac{1}{8}$. If you are asked what $12\frac{1}{2}\%$ of 24 is, this is by no means as formidable as it sounds; you need only consider it as $\frac{1}{8} \times 24$, to which the answer is obviously $^{24}\!/_{8}$, or 3. In the same way, $37\frac{1}{2}\% = \frac{3}{8}$, $62\frac{1}{2}\% = \frac{5}{8}$, and $87\frac{1}{2}\% = \frac{7}{8}$.

Something which, on the face of it, may seem even more complicated is an expression such as $33\frac{1}{3}\%$. Change the $\frac{1}{3}$ to a decimal form first and it becomes $0.333333333 \ldots$ This means that $33\frac{1}{3}\%$ is equal to $33.333333333 \ldots \%$. Move the decimal point two places leftward to remove the per cent sign and you have $0.333333333 \ldots$ But that is, after all, only $\frac{1}{3}$. Consequently, $33\frac{1}{3}\% = \frac{1}{3}$ and $33\frac{1}{3}\%$ of 15 is easily seen to be 5. In the same way $66\frac{2}{3}\% = \frac{2}{3}$, $16\frac{2}{3}\% = \frac{1}{6}$, and $83\frac{1}{3}\% = \frac{5}{6}$.

There is no particular problem with percentages over 100%. For instance, 150% is 1.5 (after the decimal point is moved two places to the left and the unnecessary zero at the extreme right is dropped) or $1\frac{1}{2}$ or $\frac{3}{2}$. Again, $233\frac{1}{3}\%$ is equal to 2.333333 . . . or to $2\frac{1}{3}$ or $\frac{7}{3}$; $512\frac{1}{2}\%$ is 5.125 or $5\frac{1}{8}$ or $\frac{41}{8}$, and so on.

Sometimes you may be given the value of a particular per cent of a particular number and wish to know the number itself. You may be told that 20% of a certain number is 16 and then asked for the number.

If 20% of a number is 16, we must nevertheless realize that 100% of that same number is the number itself. After all, 100% = 1 and any number times 1 is that number itself.

Since 100% is five times as great as 20%, the number is five times as great as the percentage. Now, $5 \times 16 = 80$ and that is the original number.

If, however, you were told that $37\frac{1}{2}\%$ of a certain number was 15 and were asked for the number, you might find it easier to work out the problem by way of fractions. Thus, $37\frac{1}{2}\% = \frac{3}{8}$, so that the problem states that $\frac{3}{8}$ of a certain number is $15. On the other hand, $\frac{8}{8}$ of that number is the number itself. Since $\frac{8}{8} \div \frac{3}{8} = \frac{8}{8} \times \frac{8}{3} = 1 \times \frac{8}{3} = \frac{8}{3}$, the number is $\frac{8}{3}$ times the percentage. It is easy to see that $\frac{8}{3} \times 15 = \frac{8}{1} \times 5 = 40$. That is the original quantity. Another and perhaps even easier route is to say that if 15 is $\frac{3}{8}$ of a number then $15 \div 3$ (or 5) is $\frac{3}{8} \div 3$ or $\frac{1}{8}$ of a number. If $\frac{1}{8}$ of a number is 5, then $\frac{8}{8}$ of a number is 5×8, or 40.

CHANGING FRACTIONS INTO WHOLE NUMBERS

There is no question that whole numbers are easier to handle than fractions. Whole numbers are even easier to handle than decimals, for with whole numbers the position of the decimal point need not bother us. Therefore, if there is any chance of changing fractions, or mixed numbers, into whole numbers, we ought to jump at it. Suppose, for instance, you wanted to work out $244 \times 2\frac{1}{2}$. You could do this in several ways. If you consider $2\frac{1}{2}$ to be $2 + \frac{1}{2}$ (as you can), then you can multiply 244 first by 2, then by $\frac{1}{2}$, and add the products. Since $244 \times 2 = 488$ and $244 \times \frac{1}{2} = 122$, the answer is $488 + 122$, or 610.

Again, you might switch to decimals. Since $2\frac{1}{2}$ can be written 2.5, the problem becomes 244×2.5. To multiply 244 by 25, you would multiply 244 by 100 (24,400) and divide by 4 to get 6100. Then, since you were multiplying by 2.5 rather than by 25, you would move the decimal point one place to the left and 6100 would become 610, which is the answer.

Or you might remember that if you multiply one number in a multiplication by a certain amount and divide the other number by the same amount you leave the product unchanged. Suppose you multiply $2\frac{1}{2}$ by 2. The product is 5. If you also divide 244 by 2 you get 122. In other words, $244 \times 2\frac{1}{2}$ can be written without any trouble as 122×5 and suddenly the mixed number is gone and you are dealing only with whole numbers.

Of course, $122 \times 5 = 122 \times 10 \div 2 = 1220 \div 2 = 610$.

Better still, you can multiply $2\frac{1}{2}$ by 4 to get 10, and divide 244 by 4 to get 61. In that case, $244 \times 2\frac{1}{2}$ becomes 61×10, which is 610 at a glance.

This system can work for a great many mixed numbers. Thus, $3\frac{1}{2}$ can be doubled to 7; $5\frac{1}{2}$ can be doubled to 11; and $7\frac{1}{2}$ can be doubled to 15.

Instead of trying to work out $66 \times 3\frac{1}{2}$ directly, you can change it to 33×7, and the answer is 231. Again, $306 \times 5\frac{1}{2}$ becomes 153×11, which is $1530 + 153 = 1683$. And $644 \times 7\frac{1}{2}$ can be written 322×15, which is $3220 + 1610$, or 4830.

The mixed number $12\frac{1}{2}$ can be doubled to 25, or it can be multiplied by 8 to give 100. Thus, $288 \times 12\frac{1}{2}$ can be written as 144×25 or, better yet, as 36×100, and there is the answer, 3600. If the number is $112\frac{1}{2}$, then remember that $112\frac{1}{2} \times 8 = 900$. That means that $96 \times 112\frac{1}{2} = 12 \times 900 = 10,800$. Or you might consider $112\frac{1}{2}$ as equal to $100 + 12\frac{1}{2}$. Therefore, $96 \times 112\frac{1}{2} = 96 \times (100 + 12\frac{1}{2})$. Since $96 \times 100 = 9600$ and $96 \times 12\frac{1}{2} = 12 \times 100 = 1200$, the answer is $9600 + 1200 = 10,800$.

All this works very much the same way in division. The big difference is that when two numbers are multiplied, one must be enlarged and the other correspondingly made small if the product is to be left unchanged; whereas in division both dividend and divisor must be made larger, or both must be made smaller. In other words, if you multiply the divisor by 2 you must also multiply the dividend by 2.

Therefore, when faced with the problem $25 \div 2\frac{1}{2}$, a glance should suffice to show you that this can be written $50 \div 5$ and that the answer is therefore 10. Consider, too, that $3\frac{1}{3} \times 3 = 10$. Therefore, if you are considering $31 \div 3\frac{1}{3}$, you need only multiply both dividend and divisor by 3 and the problem becomes $93 \div 10$. The answer is, as you see at once, 9.3, or $9\frac{3}{10}$, whichever you prefer.

You will have no trouble seeing that $21 \div 3\frac{1}{2}$ can be written $42 \div 7$ and that the answer is clearly 6. Again, $42 \div 12\frac{1}{2}$ can be written $84 \div 25$ or, better still, $336 \div 100$, so the answer is 3.36.

In principle, this is a possible technique for handling any mixed number. If a fraction is multiplied by the value of its denominator, it becomes a whole number. (In algebraic symbols, we would say $a/b \times b = a$.) If, then, you are faced with $3^{10}\!/_{13}$, you can multiply it by 13. You have the problem $(3 + {}^{10}\!/_{13}) \times 13 = 39 + 10 = 49$.

Now then, if it is a matter of a multiplication such as $39 \times 3^{10}\!/_{13}$, you divide the multiplicand by 13 and multiply the multiplier by 13 and get $3 \times 49 = 3 \times (50 - 1) = 150 - 3 = 147$. If it were a division: $2 \div 3^{10}\!/_{13}$, you multiply both dividend and divisor by 13, so that the problem becomes $26 \div 49$, or ${}^{26}\!/_{49}$.

Let me end, then, by considering the moral of the book once again.

Watch what you are doing when you calculate, and try to see the sense in all the operations, whether the slow-but-sure school rules or the quick shortcuts. If you do that you will be able to see for yourself what quick and easy methods you can adopt in particular cases.

With practice you will then begin to take such short-cuts automatically. You will, without taking any special pains, begin to convert hard problems into easy ones and you will learn when and how to get approximate answers instead of exact ones.

In the end you will not only save time and make fewer mistakes; you will find that there is actual enjoyment in manipulating figures. You will find that numbers are old and faithful friends who are not there to trip you up but to help you.

In short, arithmetic will become fun instead of work.

Index